W9-DJQ-957

Thomas G. Mezger

Applied Rheology

With Joe Flow
on Rheology Road

Anton Paar GmbH

Copyright © 2014 Anton Paar GmbH, Austria.
ISBN 978-3-9504016-0-8

Published by Anton Paar GmbH. Printed in the EU.
Translated from the German version, Angewandte Rheologie.
Translation: Christiane Sprinz and Alison Green

Anton Paar GmbH
Anton-Paar-Str. 20
8054 Graz, Austria
Tel.:   +43 316 257-0
Fax: +43 316 257-257
Email: info@anton-paar.com
Web: www.anton-paar.com

9th edition November 2021
8th edition January 2021
7th edition March 2020
6th edition March 2019
5th edition March 2018
4th edition May 2017
3rd edition November 2016
2nd edition September 2015
1st edition January 2015

Layout: Werbeagentur Rypka GmbH, 8143 Dobl/Graz, www.rypka.at

Subject to change without notice | XRRIA001EN-F

Contents

Introduction

Introduction and starting point for the stroll
along Rheology Road

They are everywhere: Fluids that flow at different
speeds and solids that can be deformed to a
certain extent. For example water, oil, honey,
shampoo, hand cream, toothpaste, sweet jelly, plastic
materials, wood, and metals. Depending on their physical behavior,
you can line these products up in a certain order: On the far left are
the liquids, on the far right the solids, and in between there are all
other highly viscous, sticky, and semi-solid substances *(Figure 0.1)*.

Joe Flow is here to assist you in the classification and description of
these materials. He is an expert in the fields of rheology and rheometry *(Figure 0.2)*. **Rheology** is used to describe and assess the
deformation and flow behavior of materials. **Rheometry** is the term
used for everything connected to the **measurement of rheological
data**.

*Figure 0.1: All lined up: Substances from daily life. From left to right:
Fluids, semi-solid and solid materials.*

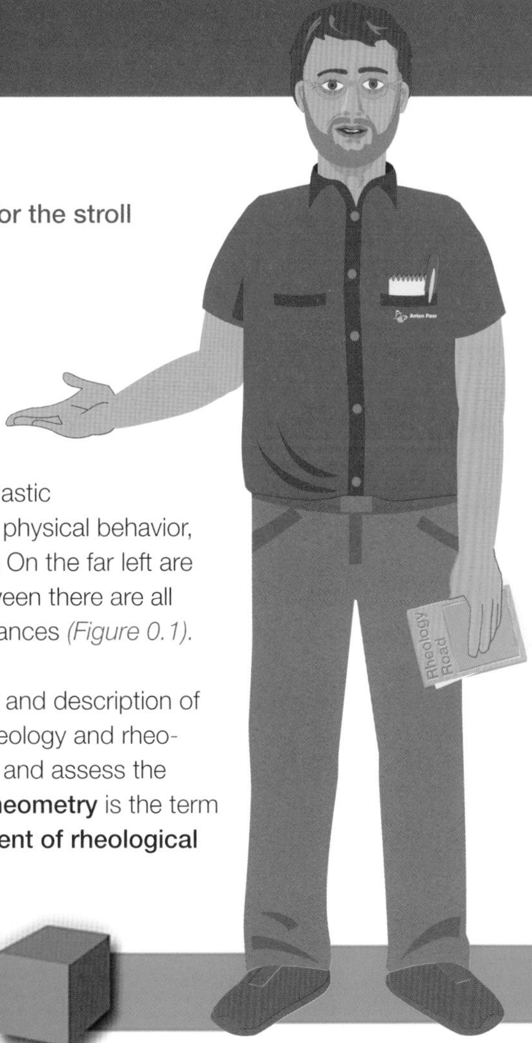

*Figure 0.2: Joe Flow is your guide
through the world of rheology and
rheometry.*

Imagine that you were to build a small house over each of the substances mentioned above. After this you could take a stroll along the row of houses just as you would on any street. Let us call this street that only exists in our imagination **Rheology Road**.

Between the beginning and the end of this road there are liquids with viscous behavior at one end and solids with elastic behavior at the other. Or, in rheological terms: On the left side, there are fluids that have an **ideal-viscous** behavior, for example water and oil (see *Chapter 6)*. The cube on the far right side is a symbol for the deformation behavior of **ideal-elastic materials**, which are very rigid and stiff, such as stones and steel *(Chapter 14)*.

In between, there are substances that act in a viscoelastic way, showing a mixture of viscous and elastic properties. The substances on the left side of the road are the **viscoelastic fluids** *(Chapters 4 to 11, 14 to 18, 20)*. The key property of these substances is that they are in a liquid state. However, when they are subjected to a rapid and large deformation, they can be prone to roping. In this event they show some elastic behavior. Examples are shampoo, glues and dough. On the right side of the road there are the **viscoelastic solids** *(Chapters 11 to 20)*. At rest they show a rigid consistency. However, when a sufficiently large force is applied, some of these materials can be easily deformed. If the deformation force is very high, the substances will finally, more or less, start to flow or break in a brittle way. Examples of such substances include lotions, creams, toothpaste, gels and soft erasers.

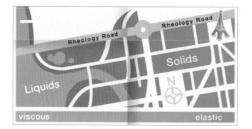

Figure 0.3:
This is a map of Rheology Road. It stretches from the "District of Liquids" on the left with fluids displaying a viscous flow behavior to the "District of Solids" on the right where the materials have an elastic deformation behavior.

Joe Flow is pleased that you selected him to be your guide on the stroll along Rheology Road. He would like to provide helpful information for all users of **rotational and oscillatory rheometers** in order to make measurements useful, no matter what type of sample is to be tested. The stroll along Rheology Road in this book starts on the left side at the "District of Liquids" and ends on the right side at the "District of Solids" *(Figure 0.3)*.

To facilitate this discovery tour, all signs and symbols, abbreviations, Greek characters, units and standards are listed in the Appendix, which also features a comprehensive subject index. In the list of references you will find text books (for example *[3], [6] and [8]*) and e-learning CDs *[1]* that provide in-depth information on the subject for the interested user.

1. Rheology and viscous behavior

Rheology is a branch of physics. Rheologists describe the deformation and flow behavior of any kind of material. The term originates from the Greek word "rhei" meaning "to flow" *(Figure 1.1)*. Rheometry is the measuring technology used to determine rheological properties.

What is **viscosity?**
All liquids are composed of molecules; dispersions also contain some significantly larger particles. When put into motion, molecules and particles are forced to slide along each other. They develop a **flow resistance** caused by **internal friction**.
Larger components present in a fluid are the reason for higher viscosity values.

Why is that so?
Molecules in fluids come in different sizes: solvent molecules approx. 0.5 nm, polymers approx. 50 nm (coiled ball diameter at rest), and mineral particles approx. 5 μm = 5000 nm. One nanometer (1 nm) equals 10^{-9} m; one micrometer (1 μm) is equal to 10^{-6} m. This means that the size ratio between molecules and particles is in the range from 1:100 to 1:10,000 *(Figure 1.2)*.

Figure 1.1: Bottle from the 19th century bearing the inscription "Tinct(ura) Rhei Vin(osa) Darel(ii)". Exhibited in the German Apotheken-Museum (Drugstore Museum), Heidelberg. The term "rhei" indicates that the content of the bottle is liquid.

The ratio of 1:1000 can be illustrated with the following figure: The molecules are fish, each of them 10 cm (0.1 m) long, whereas the particles are ships with a length of 100 m *(Figure 1.3)*.

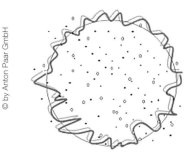

Figure 1.2: Comparison of sizes: solvent molecules (dots), polymer molecules (small circles), and particles (red outline). Viscosity is the internal friction that occurs when all components in a flowing liquid are forced to slide along each other.

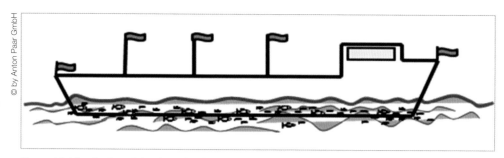

Figure 1.3: Visualization of the size ratio of 1:1000, which is similar to the size ratio of molecules and particles in a fluid. It can be compared with the size difference between small fish and large ships.

2. Simple methods for measuring viscosity

If you want to describe the flow behavior and deformation of matter in everyday language, you will probably use terms such as thick and thin, soft and solid.

a) Spatula test

The sample to be tested is scooped up with a spatula; the spatula is then held in a horizontal position or slightly tilted while pointing down. This very simple test shows that a thick, highly viscous, non-flowable paste will stick to the spatula for a prolonged time without dripping, whereas a thinner, low-viscosity dispersion will run off quite quickly due to its own weight *(Figure 2.1)*.

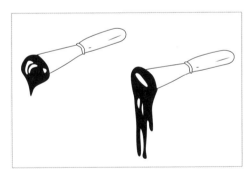

Figure 2.1: Spatula test: Is the sample's viscosity thick or thin [9]?

b) Finger test

This test is used to feel the firmness, stiffness, brittleness, stickiness or **tack** of pastes, adhesives, printing inks, lubricating grease, bitumen or dough. "Long" behavior means that the sample is prone to **stringiness**, while "short" behavior means a **brittle fracture** without stringiness *(Figure 2.2)*.

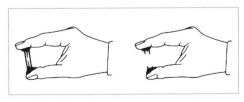

Figure 2.2: Finger test to determine the tack: Does the sample show long (stringiness) or short (sudden brittle fracture) behavior [9]?

How does the material break? Into crumbs? As a cream or similar to butter? With long or short fibers?

c) Flow cups

Flow cups are used for simple quality-control purposes of low-viscosity liquids. The parameter measured is the **flow time** that a defined amount of liquid needs to flow through an orifice at the bottom of the cup *(Figures 2.3 and 2.4)*. The shorter the flow time, the lower the viscosity of the sample. This measurement is based on gravitational force. Therefore, please note that the viscosity data obtained with this method is always dependent on the weight or density of the sample.

Flow cups come in a variety of geometries. Most common are ISO cups and Ford cups according to ISO 2431 and ASTM D1200 *(Figure 2.5)*. Please note that, with different types of flow cups, the same flow time does not necessarily mean that the viscosity is also the same. Typical samples for such a test include mineral oils, solvent-based coatings, low-viscosity gravure and flexo printing inks. Flow cups will only deliver meaningful viscosity values for liquids with ideal-viscous flow behavior *(see Chapter 6.1)*.

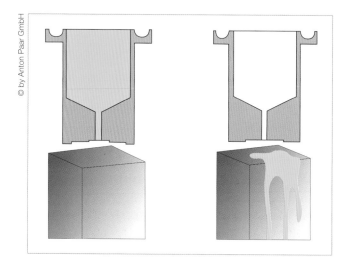

© by Anton Paar GmbH

Figure 2.3:
Flow cup for the determination of a sample's viscosity: After opening the orifice, the flow time is determined [1].

d) Falling-ball viscometers and micro falling-ball viscometers

These instruments are used to define the time a ball needs to sink or roll down over a defined distance through a liquid sample contained in a glass tube supported by gravitational force only (according to ISO 12058 and DIN 53015). To enable the visual evaluation, the sample should be transparent. The parameter measured is the viscosity, dependent on the weight or density of the sample.

If opaque samples are to be measured, it is possible to track the falling ball by means of induction in an electro-magnetic field. Specific designs are **micro falling-ball visco-meters** that are used for the smallest sample quantities such as biological fluids, protein

Figure 2.4 (left):
Flow cup measurement: The shorter the flow time, the lower the viscosity of the liquid sample.

Figure 2.5 (below):
Types of flow cups: The orifice in ISO cups (left) is longer than in Ford cups (right) [7].

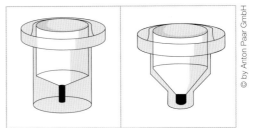

© by Anton Paar GmbH

solutions, dilute polymer solutions, low-viscosity inks and beer wort. Please note: Falling-ball viscometers, where the angle of the tube cannot be adjusted, will deliver meaningful viscosity values only for liquids with ideal-viscous flow behavior (see Chapter 6.1).

e) Glass capillary viscometers
Using these devices, the viscosity is determined by measuring the time a defined amount of liquid needs for travelling through a capillary with a defined geometry. The parameter measured is the viscosity dependent on the weight or density of the sample. Typical samples for this type of measurement include mineral oils and dilute polymer solutions. Please note: Glass capillary viscometers will deliver meaningful viscosity values only for liquids with ideal-viscous flow behavior (see Chapter 6.1).

f) Rotational tests with spindles
Using a rotational viscometer, the rotational speed of a spindle is preset after inserting the spindle into the cup containing the sample. This device measures the torque that arises from the flow resistance of the sample. Spindles are available in various geometries, including cylinders, disks, pins and cross-shaped T-bars (Figure 2.6, ISO 2555 and ISO 3219-2). In most cases, the viscosity values stated are relative values and not absolute values.

The difference is that absolute values are not correlated to the size of a measuring geometry, whereas relative values are (see Chapter 3.1). For the determination of absolute values, certain conditions for standard geometries must be complied with; for example, a narrow measuring gap that provides for consistent shear conditons. This does not apply to the spindles mentioned above and therefore they are called **relative measuring geometries**. These kinds of spindles should be used for **very simple quality control tests only.**

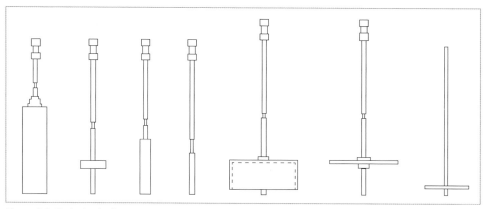

Figure 2.6: Typical spindle geometries of relative measuring systems, from the left: cylinder, disks, pins, hollow cylinder and a T-bar.

g) Rotational tests with other relative measuring geometries

Many industries use a wealth of other measuring geometries for the determination of relative viscosity values; for example, **helical stirrers** and **stirrers with perforated blades** for dispersions containing large particles (such as sand in building materials), **stirrers with inclined blades** that prevent settling of particles in dispersions (e.g. starch particles prior to gelling), **paddle stirrers, anchor-shaped rotors, rotating devices with vanes** or **laterally protruding pins, paddles** (such as the so-called **Krebs spindles for paints**, measuring the viscosity in Krebs Units or KU) as well as **ball measuring systems** (e.g. for building materials and particulate food systems with large particles, such as fruit pieces in jam or meat particles in pasta sauce; i.e., up to 10 mm), see *Figure 2.7* and ISO 3219-2.

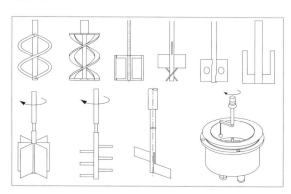

Figure 2.7: Relative measuring geometries or stirrers: helically shaped, with perforated or inclined blades, anchor shaped, as rotors with vanes or pins, as a paddle system such as the Krebs spindle for coatings, or as a ball measuring system [8].

Please note:
The viscosity values determined with relative measuring geometries are always dependent on the spindle used. Therefore, values obtained with different spindles cannot be compared with each other. In this case, it would make sense to only present raw data preset and measured by a rotational viscometer, i.e., the rotational speed and torque.

3. Rotational viscometers, oscillatory rheometers, and measuring geometries

Modern rheometers can be used for shear tests and torsional tests.
They operate with continuous rotation and rotational oscillation
(Figure 3.1).
Specific measuring systems can be used to carry out uniaxial
tensile tests either in one direction of motion or as oscillatory tests.

© by Anton Paar GmbH

*Figure 3.1: Typical rheometer for rotational tests
with continuous rotation or rotational oscillation.
When using special measuring systems, the
rheometer can be used for shear tests as well as
for tensile tests.*

Detailing the terms **viscometer** and **rheometer**: With a viscometer, only the viscosity values of a sample can be determined. This can be done via performing rotational tests, mostly speed-controlled or by use of other methods of testing. The results are presented as flow curves or viscosity curves. Rheometers are able to determine many more rheological parameters.

3.1 Absolute measuring geometries for rheometers

Absolute values, for example viscosity, can only be determined with absolute measuring geometries. In contrast to relative values, absolute values do not correlate with the size of the measuring geometry. They have a **relatively narrow shear gap** as defined by **specific standards for measuring geometries such as ISO 3219-2 and DIN 53019**. These standards describe the following measuring geometries: cone/plate, concentric cylinders and plate/plate (Figure 3.2).

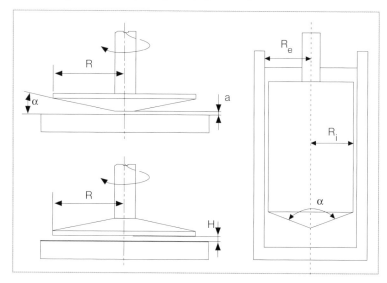

Figure 3.2:
Measuring geometries:
Cone/plate (with radius R,
cone angle α, truncation a);
plate/plate (with radius R,
distance between plates H);
and concentric cylinders
(with bob radius R_i and cup
radius R_e and internal angle α
at the tip of the bob)

a) Cone/plate (CP) or cone-and-plate measuring geometries

CP geometries are suitable for all types of fluids; however, their applicability to dispersions is limited to a certain maximum particle size. Such systems are described in the **measuring geometry standards ISO 3219-2 and DIN 53019**.

According to the ISO standard, it is recommended that a cone angle of $\alpha = 1°$ is used; cones with an angle of more than 4° are considered to be sub-standard.

For precise measurements, CP geometries with truncated cone tips are the systems of choice. The decisive parameter is the measure, a, of the gap set at the center of the cone. The rule of thumb for the **maximal acceptable particle size**, d, is: $d \leq (a/10)$.

Example: For a CP 25-1 (with a diameter of 25 mm, cone angle $\alpha = 1°$), the dimension of the truncation or gap setting for the measuring position is typically $a = 50 \ \mu m$. This means that the maximal acceptable particle size would be approximately 5 μm.

It is important to load a CP geometry with the correct sample quantity (Figure 3.3).

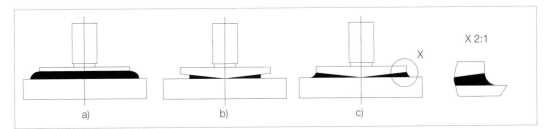

Figure 3.3: Filling of a cone/plate measuring geometry after gap setting:
a) overfilled, b) underfilled, c) correct amount (according to DIN 51810-1)

Trimming the sample:
To trim means to cut or adjust, to prune, shave or proportionate something correctly. Place the sample (use slightly more than actually needed) at the center of the lower plate. First, reduce the gap to the **trim gap position**. For CP geometries, this is the width of the measuring gap plus for example an additional 10 µm. Make sure that the gap of the measuring geometry is completely filled with the sample. Use a trimming tool (e.g. a spatula) to strip off any excess material along the brim of the plate so that the sample corresponds to the external diameter of the upper plate. Make sure that no sample material is removed from the measuring gap. Next, the final measuring gap width is approached. Due to slight overfilling, the sample will then form a small bulge at the edge.

Advantages of CP geometries:
There are uniform shear conditions in the entire conical gap. Only a small amount of the sample is required, which allows for quick temperature adjustment as well as for easy cleaning (Example: The sample volume required for a CP 25-1 is less than 0.1 ml).

Disadvantages of CP geometries:
Due to the narrow gap in the center, dispersions can only be tested up to a certain maximum particle size. At the edge of the cone, effects such as sample migration out of the gap or skin formation (drying of the sample) might occur.

Special accessories:
To prevent evaporation of solvents, a **special hood** or a **solvent trap** can be used.

b) Concentric cylinder (CC) measuring geometries
Concentric cylinder geometries are commonly used for tests on low-viscosity liquids. Such systems are specified in the **measuring geometry standards ISO 3219-2 and DIN 53019**. To ensure a relatively narrow measuring gap, the ratio of the radii of cup and bob must not exceed 1.0847.

Example: In a CC 17, the diameter of the bob is 17.0 mm, thus the diameter of the cup should be 18.44 mm (= 1.0847 x 17 mm). This means that the gap has a width of only 0.72 mm (18.44 - 17.0 mm = 1.44 / 2).

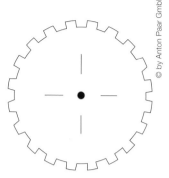

© by Anton Paar GmbH

Figure 3.4: Cross-section of a profiled cylindrical bob, used for samples that tend to have wall-slip effects

Advantages of CC geometries:

The cup is easy to fill; there is a filling level mark inside the cup. Due to the large outer surface of the cup, the temperature of the sample can be easily controlled from the outside. Fluids with low surface tension cannot flow out of the cup (as may happen with CP or PP geometries).

Disadvantages of CC geometries:

A relatively large amount of sample is required. This results in a longer temperature-equilibration time and more cleaning effort.

Special accessories:

To prevent evaporation of solvents, a **special hood** or a **solvent trap** can be used. CC systems with a **sandblasted or profiled surface** might be used to prevent wall-slip effects *(Figure 3.4)*. The surface profile depth is 0.56 mm, for example. Typical applications for these geometries are granular pastes or dispersions used as building materials. **Disposable cups and bobs** are available for hard to clean samples for single use.

c) Plate/plate or parallel plates (PP) measuring geometries

PP systems are recommended for testing pastes, gels, soft solids or highly viscous polymer melts. Such systems are described in the **measuring geometry standards ISO 3219-2, ISO 6721-10 and DIN 53019**. Recommended gap widths are from 0.5 to 1.0 mm.

Example: PP 25 means that the movable plate has a diameter of 25 mm.

Trimming the sample:

In general, the same principles apply for filling the sample into PP geometries as for CP geometries. Here, however, a larger **trim-gap position** is actually used for trimming; for example 25 µm; or even 50 µm when testing bitumen (asphalt binder).

Advantages of PP geometries:

A relatively small amount of sample is required. Due to the adjustable gap, variable measuring conditions can be set. It is also possible to test highly viscous samples (including polymer melts, uncrosslinked silicone), dispersions with larger particles, gels (with three-dimensional superstructure) and soft solids (such as cheese and elastomers). Cleaning is quick and easy.

Disadvantages of PP geometries:

There are no constant shear conditions in the gap because the shear rate at the edge of the plate is higher than at the center of the plate. At the edge of the plate, effects such as sample migration out of the gap or skin formation (drying of the sample) might occur.

Due to the relatively large gap width, there might not be a uniform sample temperature if the temperature is controlled from one side only or if the temperature-equilibration time is too short.

Special accessories:
To prevent evaporation of solvents, a **special hood** or a **solvent trap** can be used. PP geometries with **sandblasted or profiled surfaces** are available in order to prevent wall-slip effects. Typical applications include oil- and fat-containing samples from the food, cosmetics, pharmaceutical and medical fields. For samples with curing, or which are difficult to clean, there are **disposable PP geometries** available consisting of a disposable plate and a disposable dish for single use *(Figure 3.5)*. Typical applications are reaction resins and powder coatings.

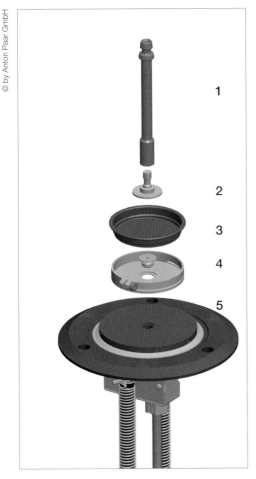

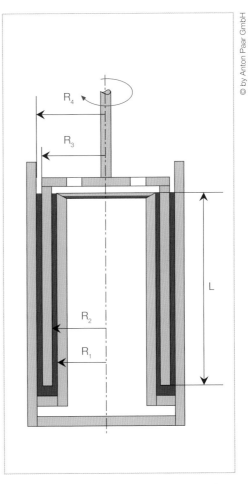

Figure 3.5: Exploded view of a disposable-plate measuring system with shaft (1), disposable plate (2), disposable dish (3) and dish holder (4) which is mounted to the bottom temperature control plate of the rheometer (5).

Figure 3.6: Double-gap measuring geometry with the four radii R1 to R4 resulting from the shape of the cup showing the geometry of a circular gap, from the hollow cylinder bob, as well as from the length L of the immersed part of the bob

d) Double-gap measuring geometries (DG)

According to **ISO 3219-2**, DG systems have a special geometry that provides for a large contact area between the sample and the surface of the DG geometry *(Figure 3.6)*. These systems enable testing at high torque resolution, and are used in particular for testing **low-viscosity liquids** such as water.

3.2 Ball bearings and air bearings for rheometers

Every drive needs a bearing; this also applies to the motor of a rheometer. However, mechanical bearings such as ball bearings show a certain **bearing friction** that should not be neglected, as it may affect the precision of rheometrical measurements.

In a **ball bearing**, for example, the balls in the pathway roll between the stator (static outer ring) and the rotor (rotating inner ring), which is connected to the rotating shaft of the rheometer. Such a bearing generates a certain amount of rolling friction in the form of a braking torque. This may result in incorrect measuring results, in particular in the lower rotational speed and torque ranges.

For testing low-viscosity fluids, such as water, at low torques with the highest precision, users prefer advanced rheometers equipped with **air bearings**. With these instruments, there is only compressed air present in the gap between the rotor and the stator of the drive. This means that a **compressed-air connection** is required for the operation of the rheometer.

4. Definition of terms: Shear stress, shear rate, law of viscosity, kinematic viscosity

The Two-Plates Model is used to define the rheological parameters needed for a scientific description of flow behavior *(Figures 4.1 and 4.2)*.

Shear is applied to a sample sandwiched between the two plates. The lower stationary plate is mounted on a very rigid support, and the upper plate can be moved parallel to the lower plate.

Before calculating the viscosity, it is necessary to first define the shear stress and the shear rate.

Figure 4.1: Two-Plates Model for shear tests: Shear is applied to the sample sandwiched between the two plates when the upper plate is set in motion, while the lower plate is stationary. The figure is an idealized illustration of the sample's individual planar fluid layers, which are displaced in relation to each other [1].

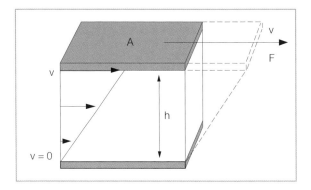

Figure 4.2:
Calculation of shear stress and shear
rate using the Two-Plates Model with
shear area A, gap width h,
shear force F, and velocity v

a) Shear stress

Definition: τ = F / A

with shear stress τ (pronounced: *tau*), shear force F (in N, newton) and shear area A (in m²), see *Figures 4.3 and 4.4*.

The **unit for shear stress** is 1 N/m² = **1 Pa (pascal)**.

The shear stress is calculated by the software. The following data are required for the calculation: A rheometer records the shear force via the torque at each measuring point. The torque is either preset or, if the rotational speed is the preset value, it is determined via the flow resistance force of the sample. The size of the shear area is also known for the measuring geometry used.

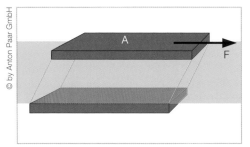

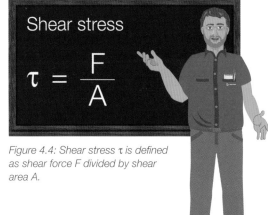

Figure 4.3: Two-Plates Model used to define the shear stress using the parameters shear force F and shear area A of the upper, movable plate

Figure 4.4: Shear stress τ is defined as shear force F divided by shear area A.

b) Shear rate

Definition: $\dot{\gamma}$ = v / h

with shear rate $\dot{\gamma}$ (pronounced: *gamma dot*), velocity v (in m/s) and shear gap h (in m), see *Figures 4.5 and 4.6*.

The **unit for shear rate** is **1/s = 1 s⁻¹,** also called reciprocal seconds.

The shear rate is calculated by the software. The following data are required for the calculation: A rheometer records the velocity as the rotational speed at each measuring

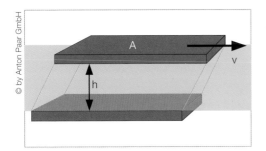

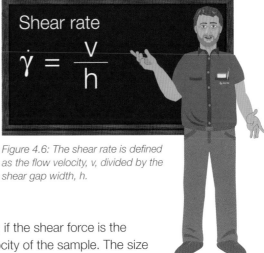

Figure 4.5: Two-Plates Model used to define the shear rate using the parameters velocity, v, of the upper, moveable plate and distance, h, between the plates

Figure 4.6: The shear rate is defined as the flow velocity, v, divided by the shear gap width, h.

point. The rotational speed is either preset or, if the shear force is the preset value, it is determined via the flow velocity of the sample. The size of the shear gap is also known for the measuring geometry used. Sometimes the following terms are used as synonyms for shear rate: **(shear) strain rate, (shear) deformation rate, shear gradient.**

Practical applications and the corresponding typical shear rates:
1) Low-shear range
is the range with very low shear rates or even shear conditions very close to the state at rest. This includes all shear rates below 1 s^{-1}.
Examples: **sedimentation of dispersions** at between 0.001 and 0.01 s^{-1};
levelling of coatings at between 0.01 and 0.1 s^{-1};
sagging of coatings at between 0.01 and 1 s^{-1} *(Figure 4.7)*

2) Medium-shear and high-shear ranges include all shear rates above 1 s^{-1}.
Examples:
- **Dip coating** from 1 to 100 s^{-1}
- **Extrusion** from 10 to 1000 s^{-1}
- **Pipe flow, pumping, filling, mixing, stirring processes** from 10 to 10,000 s^{-1}
- **Painting, brushing** from 100 to 10,000 s^{-1}
- **Spraying** from 1000 to 10,000 s^{-1}
- **High-speed blade coating** from 100,000 to 1,000,000 s^{-1}

Figure 4.7: The levelling and sagging behavior of a coating after application with a brush is an example of very low shear rates. Will any brush marks remain on the paint surface or will the surface turn out to be shiny and glossy?

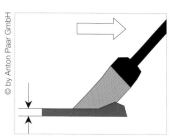

Figure 4.8: Application of paint with a brush: Demonstration of calculating the shear rate based on the application velocity and the thickness of the wet paint layer

Figure 4.9: Squeezing toothpaste out of a tube: Demonstration of calculating the shear rate based on discharged volume, flow time and radius of the tube's nozzle

Examples for the calculation of shear rates

a) Painting with a brush *(Figure 4.8)*

Calculation of the shear rate using the Two-Plates Model and the following definition:

$\dot{\gamma} = v / h$

With a painting speed of $v = 0.5$ m/s and a thickness of the wet layer of $h = 200$ μm $= 0.2$ mm $= 0.0002$ m, the resulting shear rate is 2500 s^{-1}

b) Flow of toothpaste out of a tube *(Figure 4.9)*

The shear rate of **flow in capillaries, tubes, and pipes** is calculated using the **Hagen/Poiseuille formula:**

$\dot{\gamma} = (4 \cdot V) / (\pi \cdot R^3 \cdot t)$

With a discharged volume of $V = 1$ cm^3 and a flow time of $t = 1$ s, the volume flow rate is $V/t = 10^{-6}$ m^3/s. Based on a tube outlet with a diameter $d = 6$ mm or radius $R = 3 \cdot 10^{-3}$ m and circle constant $\pi = 3.14$, the shear rate is:

$\dot{\gamma} = (4 \cdot 10^{-6}$ m^3/s$) / (\pi \cdot 27 \cdot 10^{-9}$ m$^3) = 47.2$ s^{-1} = approx. 50 s^{-1}

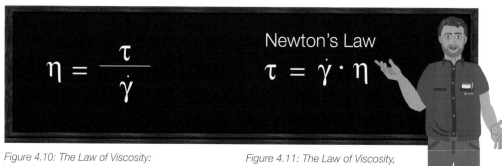

Figure 4.10: The Law of Viscosity: Viscosity η is defined as shear stress τ divided by shear rate $\dot{\gamma}$.

Figure 4.11: The Law of Viscosity, here depicted as follows: shear stress τ is shear rate $\dot{\gamma}$ times viscosity η.

c) Viscosity or shear viscosity

Definition: $\eta = \tau / \dot\gamma$

with viscosity η (pronounced: *eta*), shear stress τ (in Pa) and shear rate $\dot\gamma$ (in s^{-1}), see *Figures 4.10 and 4.11*.

This is called the **Law of Viscosity,** often also named "Newton's Law", after I. Newton (1643 to 1727). In fact, the law was formulated in this form some time later, for example in 1845 by G.G. Stokes (1819 to 1903).

η is sometimes also termed "dynamic viscosity". However, as this term is used in the literature with different meanings, it is not used in this book (see also [8]).

The unit for shear viscosity is **1 Pas = 1000 mPas (pascal seconds, milli-pascal-seconds)**. Other units include 1 kPas = 1,000 Pas (kilo-Pas), 1 MPas = 1,000,000 Pas (mega-Pas). A previously used unit was 1 cP = 1 mPas (centipoise, best pronounced in French).

Table 1 presents some viscosity values.

Flowing material	Viscosity values
Gases/air	0.01 to 0.02 mPas / 0.018 mPas
Water at 20 °C (at 0 / 40 / 60 / 80 / 100 °C)	1.0 mPas (1.8 / 0.65 / 0.47 / 0.35 / 0.28 mPas)
Milk, coffee cream	2 to 10 mPas
Olive oil	approx. 100 mPas
Motor oils (for example SAE 10W-30, at +23 / +50 / +100 °C)	50 to 1000 mPas (175 / 52 / 20 mPas)
Polymer melts (at T = +150 to +300 °C and at shear rates of between 10 and 1000 s^{-1})	10 to 10,000 Pas
Polymer melts (zero-shear viscosity, which means shear rates below 1 s^{-1})	1 kPas to 1 MPas
Bitumen at T = +80 / +60 / +40 / +20 / 0 °C	200 Pas / 1 kPas / 20 kPas / 0.5 MPas / 1 MPas

Table 1: Some viscosity values (at ambient temperature, unless otherwise specified)

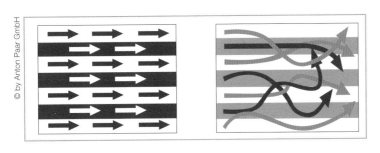

© by Anton Paar GmbH

Figure 4.12: Homogenous flow or laminar flow (left) and turbulent flow with vortex formation (right)

Please note:
The unit cP is not an SI unit and should not be used any longer.
The SI system is the international system of units
(French: *système international d'unités;* see Appendix).

All three parameters, namely shear stress, shear rate, and viscosity, can only be precisely measured if there are – as a precondition – **laminar flow conditions** and therefore there is uniform flow *(Figures 4.12 and 4.1)*. This means that **turbulent flow with vortex formation** must not occur.

d) Kinematic viscosity
Another type of viscosity is the kinematic viscosity ν (pronounced: nu).
Definition: $\nu = \eta / \rho$
with shear viscosity η (in Pas) and density ρ (in kg/m^3). The unit for kinematic viscosity is $1 \ m^2/s = 10^6 \ mm^2/s$.

For calculations, please note:
The units for density are kg/m^3 and g/cm^3, where 1000 kg/m^3 = 1 g/cm^3
A previously used unit for the kinematic viscosity was centistokes (cSt), where
1 cSt = 1 mm^2/s.

Please note:
The unit cSt is not an SI unit and should not be used any longer.

Calculation example:
A mineral oil with shear viscosity η = 1.20 Pas = 1200 mPas and density ρ = 0.900 g/cm^3 = 900 kg/m^3 has a kinematic viscosity of
$\nu = \eta / \rho = (1.2 / 900) \ m^2/s = 0.00133 \ m^2/s = 1330 \ mm^2/s$.

Kinematic viscosity is always determined if gravitational force or the weight of the sample is the driving force. This applies, for example, to tests with flow cups and falling-ball viscometers.

5. Rotational tests, introduction

Rotational tests *(Figure 5.1)* with a rheometer can be carried out in one of two operation modes, which differ in their preset parameters.

The first way is **to preset the velocity** via rotational speed or shear rate. This simulates processes that are dependent on flow velocity or volume flow rate, such as application of coatings with a brush, or of paints by spraying or flow through a tube *(Figure 5.2)*.

The second way is **to preset the driving force** via torque or shear stress. These tests simulate force-dependent applications, such as the force required to start pumping a material at rest, to squeeze sealing materials out of a cartridge, or paste out of a tube *(Figure 4.9)*.

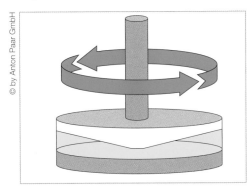

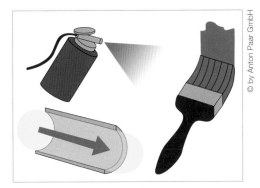

Figure 5.1: Rotational shear test on a sample; the cone rotates while the lower plate is stationary.

Figure 5.2: Shear-rate-controlled tests can be used to simulate applications that depend on flow velocity and volume flow rate, such as application of coatings with a brush, or of paints by spraying, or flow through a tube.

a) Raw data and rheological parameters for rotational tests

It is a disadvantage that the physical values determined as raw data by the rheometer are correlated to the size of the measuring geometry used. In contrast, the rheological parameters shear stress and shear rate are independent of the selected measuring geometry. They are the basis for determining the viscosity. Both modes of operation, **controlled shear rate,** CSR or CR, and **controlled shear stress,** CSS or CS, are explained in *Tables 2 and 3*.

The following applies: Torque M is in newton meter, Nm, where 1 Nm = 1000 mNm (milli-newton meter) = 10^6 µNm (micro-Nm); rotational speed n in min^{-1} meaning revolutions per minute (rpm).

Rotation with controlled shear rate (CSR)	Preset test parameters	Result
Raw data from the rheometer	Rotational speed n (in min^{-1})	Torque M (in Nm)
Rheological parameters, calculated	Shear rate $\dot\gamma$ (in s^{-1})	Shear stress τ (in Pa)

Table 2: Rotational tests with controlled shear rate (CSR), raw data and rheological parameters

Rotation with controlled shear stress (CSS)	Preset test parameters	Result
Raw data from the rheometer	Torque M (in Nm)	Rotational speed n (in min^{-1})
Rheological parameters, calculated	Shear stress τ (in Pa)	Shear rate $\dot\gamma$ (in s^{-1})

Table 3: Rotational tests with controlled shear stress (CSS), raw data and rheological parameters

For calculating the viscosity as $\eta = \tau / \dot\gamma$, the type of operation mode is irrelevant because the parameters shear stress and shear rate are both available, either as a preset value or as a result of the test.

For converting raw data into rheological parameters, there are two conversion factors available: one is used to convert the torque into the shear stress, the other for converting the rotational speed into the shear rate. They must be known for each measuring geometry; this is why the supplier always provides a data sheet for each individual measuring geometry. Additionally, they are also stored in the corresponding software program.

b) **CSR and CSS preset profiles for flow curves** *(Figure 5.3):*
1) Preset rotational speed or shear-rate ramp, usually ascending or descending in steps
2) Preset torque or shear-stress ramp, usually ascending or descending in steps
For shear rates above 1 s^{-1}, a typical setting recommended for both modes is a duration of at least one to two seconds, which is to be maintained for each measuring point because the sample needs a certain time to adapt itself to each shear step.

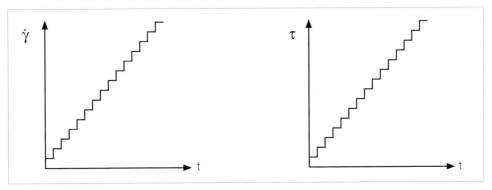

Figure 5.3: Preset profiles for flow curves as time-dependent step-like ramps, here with 15 steps which are corresponding to 15 measuring points; with controlled shear rate CSR (left) and controlled shear stress CSS (right)

6. Flow behavior, flow curve, and viscosity curve

Viscosity values are not constant values as they are affected by many conditions. You probably have already had experience in your own kitchen of salad oil, yoghurt or a highly concentrated starch suspension flowing in very different ways when stirred in a bowl or mixed with other food.

The subject of this chapter is flow behavior under shear at constant temperature.

Flow behavior can be presented in two types of diagrams *(Figure 6.1)*:
a) Flow curves with shear stress τ and shear rate $\dot{\gamma}$, usually with the latter plotted on the x-axis

b) Viscosity curves with viscosity η and shear rate $\dot{\gamma}$ (or shear stress τ), usually with the latter plotted on the x-axis. Applying the Law of Viscosity, each measuring point is calculated as follows:
$\eta = \tau / \dot{\gamma}$

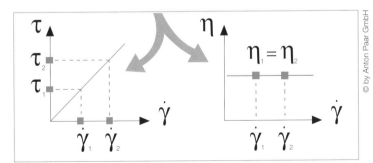

© by Anton Paar GmbH

Figure 6.1: The flow curve (left) results from the individual measuring points by plotting shear stress versus shear rate. Next, the viscosity function is calculated (right).

The advantage of diagrams on a logarithmic scale is that a range of very small values can be illustrated clearly on the same diagram as much larger values. This is not possible with a linear scale. Often the biggest changes in viscosity just take place within the range of low shear rates, which is below $\dot{\gamma} = 1\ s^{-1}$. With a presentation on a linear scale, however, this range can only be depicted to a limited extent.

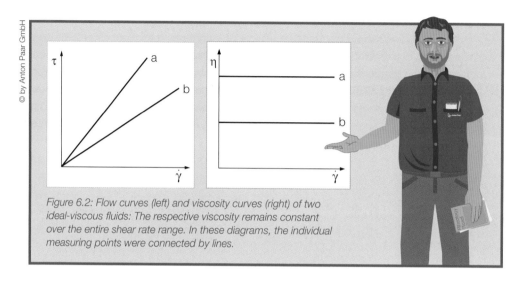

© by Anton Paar GmbH

Figure 6.2: Flow curves (left) and viscosity curves (right) of two ideal-viscous fluids: The respective viscosity remains constant over the entire shear rate range. In these diagrams, the individual measuring points were connected by lines.

6.1 Ideal-viscous flow behavior

The terms **ideal-viscous** and **Newtonian flow behavior** are synonyms (Figure 6.2). Typical materials from this group include water, mineral oil, silicone oil, salad oil, solvents such as acetone, as well as viscosity standards (e.g. calibration oils).

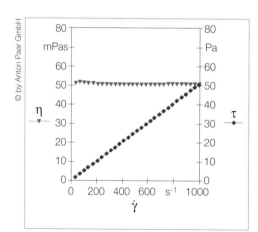

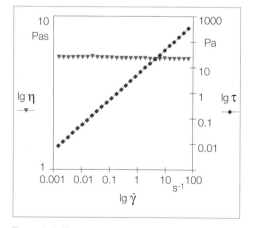

Figure 6.3: Flow curve and viscosity curve of a mineral oil, presented on a linear scale. Across the entire measuring range, the viscosity of the mineral oil remains constant, thus showing ideal-viscous flow behavior.

Figure 6.4: Flow curve and viscosity curve of an ideal-viscous silicone oil, presented on a logarithmic scale for better illustration of the values in the low shear range.

What is the viscosity value of water
at ambient temperature?
This is an interesting question and not
just for world record swimmers.

© by Anton Paar GmbH

Figure 6.5: With Joe Flow at the swimming pool ...

Measuring example:
Flow curve and viscosity curve of a mineral oil *(Figure 6.3).*
A mineral oil was tested using a cylinder geometry at a temperature of T = +50 °C.
The shear-rate-controlled test was carried out with 30 measuring points in a step-like
ascending arrangement. Total measuring time was t = 180 s; this corresponds to 6 s for
each measuring point. The evaluation shows that the viscosity remains constant across
the entire measuring range. Thus the oil displays ideal-viscous behavior.

Measuring example: Flow curve and viscosity curve of a silicone oil *(Figure 6.4)*
A silicone oil was tested in a cone/plate geometry at a temperature of T = +23 °C.
A shear-rate-controlled test was carried out using ascending logarithmic steps. The
duration for each measuring point was decreased continuously with increasing shear
rates, starting at a shear rate of 0.001 s^{-1} with 1000 s for each measuring point and
ending at a shear rate of 1000 s^{-1} with only 1 s for each measuring point.
The evaluation shows that the viscosity remains constant over the entire measuring
range, even at very low shear rates. Thus the silicone oil displays ideal-viscous behavior.
A diagram on a logarithmic scale was chosen for the presentation, which allows the
values even at low shear rates to be displayed very clearly.

Measuring example: Flow curve and viscosity curve of water *(Figures 6.5 and 6.6)*
Water was tested in a double-gap geometry at a temperature of T = +20 °C.
A shear-rate-controlled test was carried out using ascending logarithmic steps.

As expected, the water showed a constant viscosity of $\eta = 1$ mPas, which is ideal-viscous behavior.

The presentation in the diagram was limited to a shear-rate range of between 0.2 and 200 s⁻¹. At lower shear rates, the detectable torque signal would be too small under these measuring conditions. At higher shear rates, turbulent-flow effects in the gap would cause disturbances to the flow. There is no way of preventing such effects when testing fast-flowing low-viscosity liquids. In this case, the requirements for a scientifically precise calculation of the viscosity would not be met because the precondition is laminar flow.

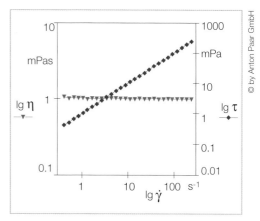

Figure 6.6: Flow curve and viscosity curve of water, tested in a double-gap geometry at T = +20 °C: Within the shear rate range shown (0.2 to 200 s⁻¹), water displays ideal-viscous flow behavior with $\eta = 1$ mPas.

6.2 Shear-thinning flow behavior

Shear-thinning and **pseudoplastic flow behavior** are synonyms. This behavior is characterized by decreasing viscosity with increasing shear rates (Figure 6.7). Typical materials that show this behavior are coatings, glues, shampoos, polymer solutions and polymer melts.

Since viscosity is shear-dependent, it should always be given with the shear condition. Example: $\eta_1(\dot{\gamma}_1) = 0.50$ Pas (at 10 s⁻¹) and $\eta_2(\dot{\gamma}_2) = 0.10$ Pas (at 100 s⁻¹).

Measuring example:
Comparison of the viscosity curves of a mineral oil and a polymer solution
(Figure 6.8)

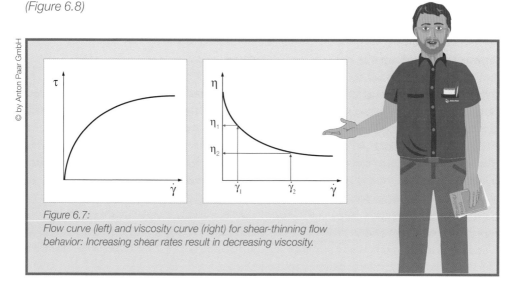

Figure 6.7:
Flow curve (left) and viscosity curve (right) for shear-thinning flow behavior: Increasing shear rates result in decreasing viscosity.

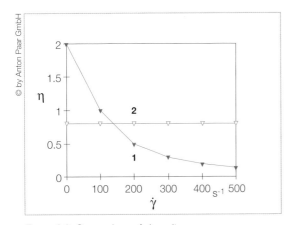

Figure 6.8: Comparison of viscosity curves: (1) shear-thinning polymer solution and (2) ideal-viscous mineral oil

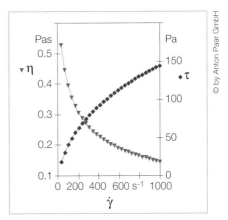

Figure 6.9: Typical example of polymer solutions: flow curve and viscosity curve of a water-based methyl cellulose solution with shear-thinning flow behavior.

The flow behavior of a motor oil and a water-based solution of wallpaper paste at an ambient temperature (T = +20 °C) was compared. The measurement was carried out as a controlled-shear-rate test. The diagram shows that the mineral oil displays constant viscosity, thus ideal-viscous flow behavior. In contrast, the viscosity function of the polymer solution shows continuously decreasing viscosity indicating shear-thinning flow behavior.

Measuring example:
Flow curve and viscosity curve of a polymer solution *(Figure 6.9)*.
The sample used for the shear-rate-controlled test was a water-based methyl cellulose solution at T = +23 °C. The curves show shear-thinning behavior which is typical for polymer solutions. Presented on a linear scale, the viscosity curve does not drop steeply but continuously across a large shear-rate range.

Measuring example:
Flow curve and viscosity curve of two emulsions *(Figure 6.10)*
The flow behavior of two emulsions E1 and E2 was compared at T = +20 °C. E1 was a non-diluted O/W emulsion (oil in water); for E2, E1 was diluted by adding 10% water. The measurement was carried out as a controlled-shear-rate test. Both emulsions display shear-thinning flow behavior, which is typical for dispersions. In comparison to many polymer solutions and polymer melts, the viscosity curves in the low shear range drop relatively steeply. At increased shear rates they flatten out in the higher shear-rate range when plotted on a linear scale. This behavior can be explained by the strong orientation of the particles or droplets of the inner phase, which already occurs at low shear rates. Most of the particles are then aligned in the direction of shear and thus cannot be orientated any further.

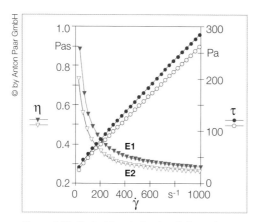

Figure 6.10: Typical flow behavior of dispersions with strongly pronounced shear thinning in the lower shear-rate range: Flow curves and viscosity curves of two emulsions - undiluted E1, and E2 with 10% water added.

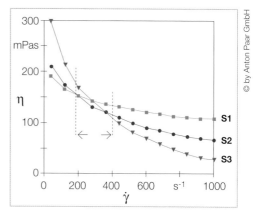

Figure 6.11: Viscosity curves of three screen-printing inks with different extents of shear-thinning flow behavior: The arrows indicate the shear-rate range covered by the flow cup used. In this range, the samples do not show any significant difference in viscosity.

Measuring example:

Comparison of viscosity of screen-printing inks using a flow cup and a rotational rheometer (Figure 6.11)

Three low-viscosity screen-printing inks S1 to S3 with the same pigment content were compared with each other. S1 was the product used so far. It contained a known binder and showed good application behavior. S3 contained a different binder, while S2 contained a 50:50 mixture of the two binding agents.

During the printing process, the three printing inks showed clear differences. However, when tested with a flow cup, the user was not able to determine any significant differences regarding the flow times of the three samples.

On the other hand, the rotational rheometer was able to distinguish clearly between the flow behavior of the three samples in the shear-rate range between 0 and 1000 s^{-1}. The reason: Flow cups can only measure within a limited shear-rate range (in this case between approx. 200 and 400 s^{-1}). Coincidentally, the viscosity values of the three samples were rather similar just in this measuring range.

Conclusion: In the case of shear-thinning behavior, single point measurements, such as with a flow cup, are not sufficient for evaluating flow behavior.

6.2.1 Internal structures of samples and shear-thinning behavior

a) Polymers

At rest, long, filamentary molecules of **uncrosslinked polymers** contract to form balls. At the edges of the molecules, the chains become **entangled** with each other (Figure 6.12). **Under shear**, the entangled balls change their shape and become ellipsoid (shaped like an American football or an airship). This deformation goes hand in hand with increasing **disentanglement** of the molecules. As individual molecules have less flow resistance than entangled superstructures, the result is shear-thinning flow behavior with decreasing viscosity values at higher shear rates.

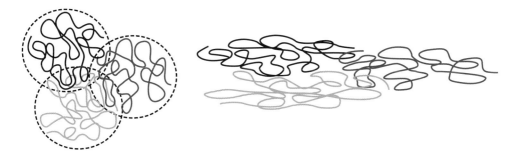

Figure 6.12: Filamentary molecules of a polymer solution or polymer melt Left: At rest with coiled and entangled molecules. Right: In motion under shear, stretched and partly disentangled molecules, oriented in the direction of shear.

Sizes:
Coiled molecules at rest have a so-called hydrodynamic **diameter** of between 5 and 50 nm. Example: The size ratio for polyethylene (PE) of molar mass M = 100 kg/mol, with filamentary molecules of approximate length L = 1 µm = 1000 nm (when stretched) and diameter of approx. d = 0.5 nm, is L/d = 2000:1. For a better understanding, just imagine one spaghetti noodle which is 1 mm thick and 2000 mm = 2 m long *(Figure 6.13)*.

b) Suspensions containing needle-shaped or platelet-like particles
In the absence of interaction forces, the particles in a suspension at rest are oriented randomly *(Figure 6.14)*. When shear is applied, the particles start to align themselves parallel to the direction of flow. This facilitates their sliding along each other more easily.

Since the individual particles now show less flow resistance than they do in an unordered state at rest, it is obvious that with increasing shear rate they display shear-thinning flow behavior with a decrease in viscosity.

Sizes:
Example 1: Pigment particles in metallic-effect automotive coatings, so-called aluminum flakes, have a diameter of d = 7 to 30 µm and a thickness of h = 0.2 to 1 µm: The resulting ratio d/h is 30:1. For a better understanding: Beer mats have a shape like this.

Figure 6.13: Similar to linear polymer molucules, cooked spaghetti also results in many entanglements.

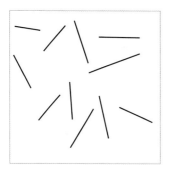 

Figure 6.14:
Needle-shaped or platelet-like particles in a suspension:
Left: Randomly arranged at rest.
Right: In motion under shear, oriented in the direction of shear.

Example 2: Ceramic primary particles in casting slurries such as montmorillonite (e.g. bentonite) are approx. 800 nm long, 800 nm wide, and 1 nm thick.

c) Suspensions with superstructures of agglomerated primary particles

At rest, agglomerates in a suspension also enclose parts of the dispersion liquid thus immobilizing it *(Figure 6.15)*. Under shear, the superstructures increasingly disintegrate into primary particles, or, to be more precise, into their aggregates. As the smaller superstructures display less flow resistance, and as the formerly immobilized dispersion liquid is now free to move again, the result is shear-thinning flow behavior with decreasing viscosity at increasing shear rates.

Sizes:

Primary particles have a size of 1 to 10 nm, while **aggregates**, with a total size of up to 100 nm, are primary particles linked with relatively strong bonds.

Agglomerates, with an overall size of up to 100 μm, are characterized by relatively loose bonds; they consist of aggregates or particles.

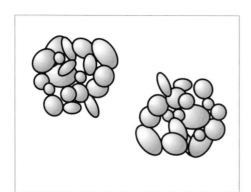 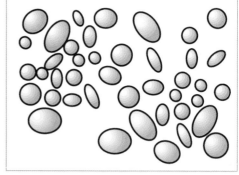

Figure 6.15: Particles in a suspension: Left: Agglomerated particles at rest.
Right: Under shear, in motion with breakdown of the superstructure. This reduces the flow resistance, thus causing shear-thinning flow behavior.

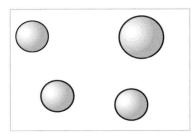 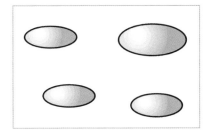

Figure 6.16: Droplets in an emulsion. Left: State at rest with sphere-like droplets. Right: In motion under shear, the droplets are deformed in the direction of shear.

d) Emulsions with dispersed droplets

At rest, the droplets in an emulsion are shaped like spheres *(Figure 6.16).* When flowing, the size and shape of the droplets are dependent on the shear applied.

Increasing deformation leads to an ellipsoid shape. Because the droplets now show a smaller cross section in the direction of flow, the emulsion displays a decrease in viscosity, i.e., shear-thinning flow behavior.

Sizes:

Droplets and fat particles in **milk** have diameters of between 0.1 and 10 μm.

Note: Emulsions with broken droplets under strong shear

It is also possible that, under high shear, **subdivision of droplets** may occur, resulting in increased viscosity. The cause may be the **increased volume-specific surface** that accompanies the breakdown of the droplets. If strong interaction forces are present at the interface between the two liquid phases, this may cause undesired results.

For example, a hand cream or lotion may feel **sticky, tacky,** or **stringy** when applied. An interesting option for optically displaying transparent substances under defined shear conditions is the use of a **rheo-microscope** *(Figure 6.17).*

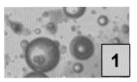 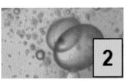 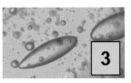 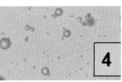

© by Anton Paar GmbH

Figure 6.17: Emulsion composed of water droplets in silicone oil, viewed under an optical microscope.
(1) At rest, the droplets are sphere shaped;
(2) At a low shear rate of 0.5 s^{-1}, the droplets of the inner phase are slightly deformed;
(3) At a shear rate of 16 s^{-1}, clearly deformed droplets are now shaped like ellipsoids (like an airship);
(4) At rest after having been subjected to a high shear rate of 100 s^{-1}, which has resulted in a breakdown of droplets and a clearly reduced mean droplet size.

6.2.2 Logarithmic flow curves and viscosity curves, and zero-shear viscosity

For evaluating behavior in the low shear-rate range, it is beneficial to use a log-log plot for the diagrams of flow curves and viscosity curves. This kind of a diagram is often used for viscosity curves of polymers with uncrosslinked molecules. Here, in the **low-shear range**, which is typically associated with **shear rates below 1 s⁻¹**, each of these viscosity curves shows a constant value, which is the so-called **plateau value of the zero-shear viscosity** η_0.

This term was chosen because in this case the shear rate approaches zero, and therefore the state at rest.

For **uncrosslinked polymers** at the same measuring temperature as well as for polymer solutions at the same concentration, the following applies: The higher the **average molar mass M of the polymer**, the higher is the value of zero-shear viscosity *(Figure 6.18)*. Furthermore, the following applies: A steeper drop in the viscosity curve in the flow range, which occurs at shear rates above 1 s⁻¹, indicates a narrower **molar mass distribution** (MMD).

Often another plateau value can be observed in the **high-shear-rate range** when almost all molecules have been completely disentangled. This value is the so-called **limiting high-shear viscosity** η_∞, which represents the viscosity at shear rates approaching an infinitely high value *(Figure 6.19)*. The high-shear range is usually associated with shear rates above 1,000 s⁻¹.

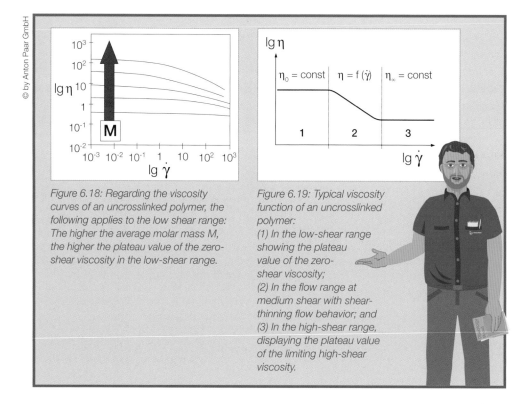

© by Anton Paar GmbH

Figure 6.18: Regarding the viscosity curves of an uncrosslinked polymer, the following applies to the low shear range: The higher the average molar mass M, the higher the plateau value of the zero-shear viscosity in the low-shear range.

Figure 6.19: Typical viscosity function of an uncrosslinked polymer:
(1) In the low-shear range showing the plateau value of the zero-shear viscosity;
(2) In the flow range at medium shear with shear-thinning flow behavior; and
(3) In the high-shear range, displaying the plateau value of the limiting high-shear viscosity.

Measuring example:
Flow curve and viscosity curve of a polymer solution on a logarithmic scale *(Figure 6.20)*

A water-based methyl cellulose solution was subjected to a shear-rate-controlled test with logarithmically ascending steps at $T = +23$ °C. The logarithmic plot clearly shows the **plateau of zero-shear viscosity** that occurs in the **low shear range at shear rates below 1 s^{-1}**. At higher shear rates, shear-thinning behavior can be observed, which is typical for polymer solutions.

Measuring example:
Comparison of the viscosity curves of two polymer solutions *(Figure 6.21)*

Two solutions of the polymers P1 and P2 were compared at $T = +20$ °C. P1 has a higher **plateau value of zero-shear viscosity** η_0 and therefore a higher average molar mass than P2. At higher shear rates, both samples display shear-thinning behavior, which is typical for polymer solutions. The steeper decline in viscosity of P1 in the flow range indicates a narrower **molar mass distribution (MMD)** compared to P2. If all polymer molecules were the same size, then the MMD would be very narrow, resulting in a very steep decline of the viscosity curve.

Measuring example:
Comparison of the viscosity curves of solutions and gels for cosmetic applications *(Figure 6.22)*

Several cosmetic products, one gel (1) and three solutions (2 to 4), were tested at $T = +23$ °C. Samples 1 to 3 were measured in a cylinder geometry, and a double gap geometry was used for sample 4. Analysis:

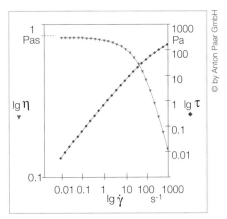

Figure 6.20: Typical flow behavior of an uncrosslinked polymer: Flow curve and viscosity curve of a water-based methyl cellulose solution, presented on a logarithmic scale for better illustrating of the plateau of zero-shear viscosity. After leaving the low-shear range, the polymer solution shows shear-thinning flow behavior.

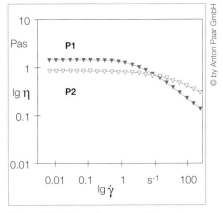

Figure 6.21: Viscosity curves of two polymer solutions: P1 shows a higher plateau value of zero-shear viscosity and therefore a higher average molar mass compared to P2. The steeper decline of the viscosity curve of P1 in the flow range indicates a narrower molar mass distribution compared to P2.

Sample 1: In the direction of decreasing shear rates, the viscosity of this **gel** increases towards infinity. This indicates a **firm texture** of the gel **at rest**. Across the entire range from 0.05 to 500 s^{-1}, the sample displays a distinct shear-thinning flow behavior. The viscosity drops by three decades from $\eta = 100$ Pas to 0.1 Pas.

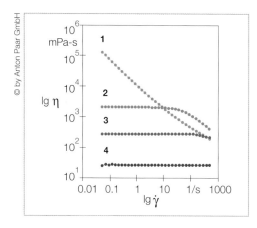

© by Anton Paar GmbH

Figure 6.22: Comparison of the viscosity curves of three solutions and one gel for cosmetic applications:
Sample 1 is a gel with a yield point because in the low-shear range the viscosity approaches infinity.
Both samples 2 and 3 show a plateau value of zero-shear viscosity, and are therefore liquids when at rest.
Sample 4 is a comparably low-viscosity liquid across the entire range and shows ideal-viscous flow behavior.

Samples 2 and 3: At rest, they are fluid and therefore **self-levelling**, as they both have a **plateau of zero-shear viscosity**. Above a shear rate of 50 s^{-1} or 100 s^{-1}, respectively, they are shear-thinning.

Sample 4 shows ideal-viscous (or Newtonian) behavior over the entire measuring range with a viscosity of η = 22 mPas.

6.3 Shear-thickening flow behavior

Shear-thickening and **dilatant flow behavior** are synonyms. In this case, the viscosity increases with increasing shear rates *(Figure 6.23)*. Materials that typically display such behavior include highly filled dispersions, such as ceramic suspensions (casting slurries), starch dispersions, plastisol pastes that lack a sufficient amount of plasticizer, dental filling masses (dental composites) as well as special composite materials for protective clothing.

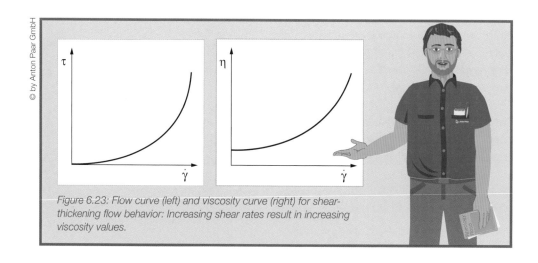

© by Anton Paar GmbH

Figure 6.23: Flow curve (left) and viscosity curve (right) for shear-thickening flow behavior: Increasing shear rates result in increasing viscosity values.

Shear-thickening flow behavior **may cause problems in technical processes**, such as breakage of the drive shaft of stirrers, blockage of spraying nozzles or insufficient mold filling in injection-molding applications.

Since viscosity values are shear-dependent, they should always be stated together with the shear rate.

Example: $\eta_1(\dot{\gamma}_1) = 0.50$ Pas (at 10 s^{-1}) and $\eta_2(\dot{\gamma}_2) = 1.00$ Pas (at 100 s^{-1}).

Measuring example:
Comparison of flow curves and viscosity curves of three starch dispersions
(Figure 6.24)
Flow behavior and viscosity of three water-based dispersions with varying starch content (sample 1 with 4%, 2 with 5% and 3 with 6% starch of the total mass) were tested at ambient temperature (T = +23 °C). The diagram clearly shows: the higher the starch content, the higher the viscosity. In the shear range up to approximately 10 s^{-1}, all three samples display shear-thinning flow behavior. At higher shear rates, however, all three samples tend to show shear-thickening. This is because the particles collide more often due to the higher velocity.

Measuring example:
Flow curve and viscosity curve of a shear-thickening ceramic suspension
(Figure 6.25)
The flow behavior of a ceramic suspension with a high solid matter content was tested. This ceramic suspension had shown **insufficient mold filling in an injection molding machine**. The evaluation reveals that, after the sample passes a viscosity minimum at a shear rate of 50 s^{-1}, the viscosity curve slopes up uniformly and continuously, therefore

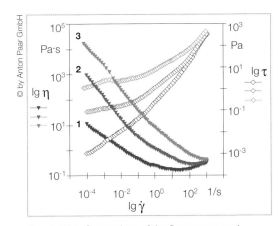

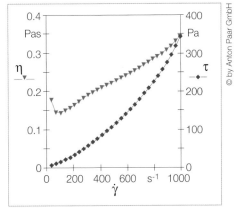

Figure 6.24: Comparison of the flow curves and viscosity curves of three dispersions with a starch content that increases from sample 1 to sample 3. Up to a shear rate of 10 s^{-1} all dispersions display shear-thinning flow behavior with a tendency to shear thickening at higher shear rates.

Figure 6.25: Flow curve and viscosity curve of a ceramic suspension. After passing the viscosity minimum, the particles disturb each other at higher shear rates, which results in shear-thickening flow behavior.

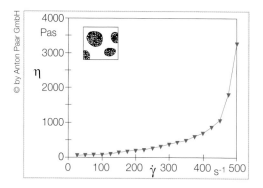

Figure 6.26: Viscosity curve of a plastisol paste with insufficient plasticizer, therefore showing shear-thickening flow behavior at T = +23 °C. Image detail on the top left: Enlarged illustration of the two plastisol components: large, compact polymer particles surrounded by plasticizer

showing shear-thickening flow behavior. In the beginning, at lower shear rates of up to approximately 50 s^{-1}, the platelet-like ceramic particles are oriented in the direction of the flow so that they can slide along each other rather easily.

After passing the viscosity minimum and reaching the range of higher shear rates, however, they increasingly disturb each other's flow. As a consequence, an irregular flow field develops, resulting in shear-thickening. In subsequent experiments, the desired shear-thinning flow behavior across the entire shear range could be achieved by either diluting the suspension with water or by adding a specific rheology additive.

Measuring example:
Viscosity curve of a shear-thickening plastisol *(Figure 6.26)*
A highly filled PVC plastisol paste was tested at an ambient temperature (T = +23 °C). Plastisols are mainly composed of two key components (phases): relatively large and compact "polymer particles" and smaller plasticizer molecules that surround the particles, as can be seen in the image detail in Figure 6.26. Shear-thickening behavior results across the entire measuring range which is very pronounced at high shear rates. Obviously, the limited amount of plasticizer is not sufficient to separate the large polymer particles in the flowing state. This type of plastisol would be unfit for spraying processes, for example in the automotive industry, because **the nozzle would clog** very easily at commonly applied volume-flow rates. This problem was later solved by increasing the amount of plasticizer.

Internal structures of samples and shear-thickening behavior
The occurrence of shear-thickening in suspensions should be expected under the following two conditions: (1) at high shear load, e.g. caused by high shear rates, and (2) when containing a high amount of solid matter (better expressed as solid/volume percentage; this is the fraction of solid particles in the total dispersion volume).
Particles in flowing dispersions are constantly subjected to rotational motion, therefore **particle shape has a big effect**. The more the shape deviates from the spherical shape, the stronger the effect *(Figure 6.27)*. This is due to the different amounts of space required by rotating particles of different shape. The result can be disturbance or even blockage of uniform flow, for example in spray-coating processes.

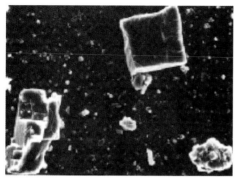 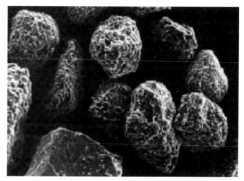

Figure 6.27: Effect of particle shape on flow behavior. With the same solid/volume percentage, the suspension containing the angular limestone particles (left) displays shear-thickening flow behavior at a lower shear rate than the suspension with the rounder particles (right) [10].

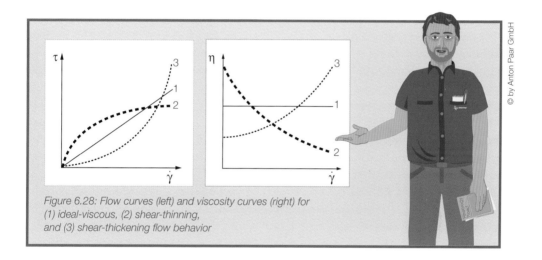

© by Anton Paar GmbH

Figure 6.28: Flow curves (left) and viscosity curves (right) for (1) ideal-viscous, (2) shear-thinning, and (3) shear-thickening flow behavior

 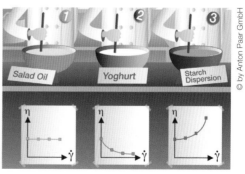

© by Anton Paar GmbH

Figure 6.29: Chefs acting as rotors and measuring sensors using their mixing spoons as bobs. With an increase in mixing speed, there is no change in viscosity for the salad oil, a constant decrease in viscosity for the yoghurt and a constant increase in viscosity for the starch dispersion [1].

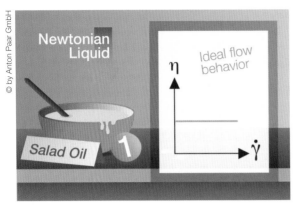

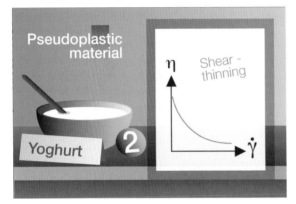

6.4 Summary of the flow behavior

Figures 6.28 to 6.30 show a comparison of the various types of flow behavior as flow curves and viscosity curves:

(1) ideal-viscous - example: salad oil,

(2) shear-thinning - example: yoghurt,

(3) shear-thickening - example: highly concentrated starch dispersion.

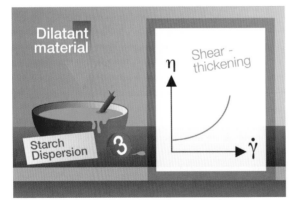

Figure 6.30: Salad oil displays ideal-viscous (Newtonian) flow behavior; yoghurt shows shear-thinning (pseudoplastic) flow behavior and the starch dispersion is shear-thickening (dilatant). The latter may cause technical problems. In our stirring contest, the third chef broke his wooden spoon.

7. Yield point, evaluation using the flow curve

The yield point is the lowest shear-stress value above which a material will behave like a fluid, and below which the material will act like a - sometimes very soft - solid matter (according to DIN/TR 91143-1).

Yoghurt, mayonnaise, ketchup, toothpaste, lipstick and sealants are typical examples of materials that have a yield point.
The yield point or yield stress is the minimum force that must be exceeded in order to break down a sample's structure at rest, and thus make it flow.

Examples of yield stress applications include **the force required to start pumping a liquid at rest** or **to squeeze toothpaste from a tube** *(Figure 7.1)* or a **silicone sealing material from a cartridge**.
A sample's superstructure can be imagined as being a stable, three-dimensional, consistent, chemical-physical network of forces interacting between the individual components of the sample; for example, between the particles of a rheology additive in a dispersion *(Figure 7.2)*. Yield-point measurements are always comparisons of the acting forces: the internal **cohesion force** of the sample's network of forces on the one side; and the external force acting upon the sample on the other side. Therefore, **tests with preset force or controlled shear stress (CSS)** will often deliver better results than tests with controlled shear rate (CSR).

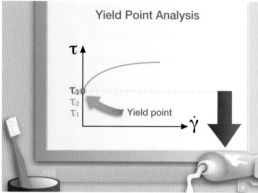

Figure 7.1: Determination of the yield point of toothpaste, here as the limiting value of a force or a shear stress. The sample flows when this value is exceeded.

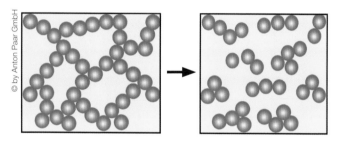

Figure 7.2:
When at rest, via their interactive forces, the particles are forming a three-dimensional, consistent, intact and stable network. The material is in a solid state (left). After the yield point has been exceeded, the superstructure breaks down and the material may start to flow (right).

From the rheological point of view, the yield point is a shear stress limit; its unit is Pa (pascal). The **yield value determined** by whatever means is **not a material constant** because it depends on the sample's pretreatment and on the measuring method used, as well as on the **evaluation method** used. This chapter describes some test methods and evaluation methods for simple quality-assurance purposes using rotational tests. More precise methods for the determination of yield point and flow point will be described later in this book *(see Chapters 13 and 15.2)*.

a) Determination of the yield point using a flow-curve diagram on a linear scale
Method 1:
Determination of the yield point via the shear-stress-axis intercept of a flow curve
With this evaluation method, the measured flow curve is presented on a linear scale. Next, the yield point is read as the value on the shear-stress axis that appears at the beginning of the flow curve *(Figure 7.3)*. This very easy method should only be used for simple quality-assurance tests. Due to limited accuracy in the range of lower shear rates, this method is not recommended for tests in research and development.

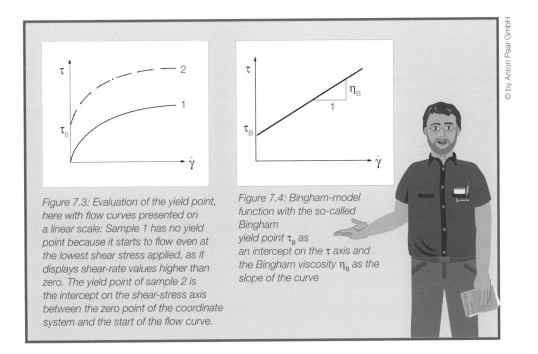

Figure 7.3: Evaluation of the yield point, here with flow curves presented on a linear scale: Sample 1 has no yield point because it starts to flow even at the lowest shear stress applied, as it displays shear-rate values higher than zero. The yield point of sample 2 is the intercept on the shear-stress axis between the zero point of the coordinate system and the start of the flow curve.

Figure 7.4: Bingham-model function with the so-called Bingham yield point τ_B as an intercept on the τ axis and the Bingham viscosity η_B as the slope of the curve

Method 2:
Determination of the yield point via mathematical curve-fitting models for flow curves

Flow curves consist of many individual measuring points. With this method, the yield point is evaluated by calculating a **curve fitting** that aims at the best possible superposition with the measured flow-curve values.

The result is stated as a mathematical function. The three following **model functions** are commonly used, however, they are only suitable for simple quality-control tests. Due to limited accuracy in the range of lower shear rates, they are not recommended for tests in research and development. In addition to that, there is a wealth of fitting models available *(see also [8])*.

1) Curve-fitting model according to Bingham

$\tau = \tau_B + \eta_B \cdot \dot{\gamma}$

with the Bingham yield point τ_B as an axis intercept and the Bingham viscosity η_B whose value is derived from the slope of the curve. This very simple model function plotted on a linear-scale flow-curve diagram shows a straight line with an intercept on the shear-stress axis *(Figure 7.4)*. Only the two evaluation parameters mentioned above are stated. In the lower shear-rate range, curve fitting is often rather imprecise.

2) Curve-fitting model according to Casson

The two fitting values here are the Casson yield point as the axis intercept and the Casson viscosity. Curve fitting is performed using the square-root function. The flow-curve diagram on a linear scale shows that the model function is shaped as a curve with

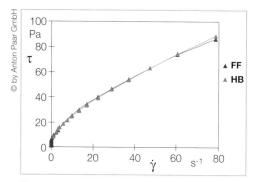

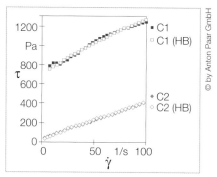

Figure 7.5: Measured flow curve of a fracturing fluid for crude-oil production and curve fitting according to the Herschel/Bulkley (HB) model; the yield point calculated here is 5.9 Pa.

Figure 7.6: Flow curves of two creams C1 and C2 (filled squares) and curve fitting according to Herschel/Bulkley (open squares): With the HB model, the yield points calculated were 705 Pa for C1 and 31.7 Pa for C2.

an intercept on the shear-stress axis (comparable with curve 2 in *Figure 7.3*). By taking the bend of the curve in the range of lower shear rates into consideration, this curve fitting model is often better than the Bingham model.

3) Curve-fitting model according to Herschel/Bulkley

In this model, the two parameters are the Herschel/Bulkley yield point as an axis intercept and the parameter p. Here again, the flow curve diagram on a linear scale shows that the model function is shaped as a curve with an intercept on the shear-stress axis (comparable with curve 2 in *Figure 7.3*). The parameter p is used to differentiate within the flow range between shear-thinning ($p < 1$), shear-thickening ($p > 1$), and Bingham flow behavior ($p = 1$). Using these evaluation parameters, in most cases a better curve fitting will be achieved than with the Bingham model.

Measuring example:
Flow curve of a fracturing fluid and evaluation according to Herschel/Bulkley
(Figure 7.5).
Determination of the flow curve of a fracturing fluid using a special pressure cell at a pressure of 3 MPa (30 bar). Such fluids are used for the production of natural gas and crude oil. Using analysis software, the model function according to Herschel/Bulkley (HB) was calculated, resulting in a yield point of 5.9 Pa.

Measuring example:
Flow curves of two creams and evaluation according to Herschel/Bulkley
(Figure 7.6).
Flow curves of the two creams C1 and C2 were compared. The yield points calculated according to the Herschel/Bulkley (HB) model were 705 Pa and 31.7 Pa, respectively. This means that for C1 a higher force is required to make the cream change from the state at rest into a flowing material when applied to the skin. Furthermore, Bingham behavior was identified within the flow range of C2 because the curve-fitting parameter

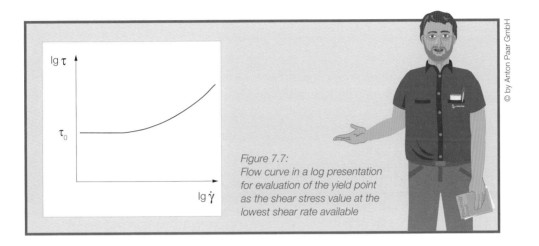

Figure 7.7:
Flow curve in a log presentation for evaluation of the yield point as the shear stress value at the lowest shear rate available

$p = 1$. The fitting curve here is a straight line. C1 had a value of $p = 0.85$ which indicates shear-thinning behavior. The fitting curve here is slightly bent.

b) Determination of the yield point using a flow curve diagram on a logarithmic scale
These methods are intended for users who are not afraid of log diagrams. When flow curves are presented and analyzed with a log/log diagram, then not only can the yield point be illustrated more descriptively (due to higher resolution of the data), but the calculation options are much more precise as well. After all, the behavior at rest and/or in the range of very low shear rates will be evaluated, and thus the preset for this test should be also performed in ascending log steps. It is recommended that a rheometer with an air bearing is used for this kind of test.

Method 3:
Reading the yield point as the shear-stress value at the lowest shear rate *(Figure 7.7)*

Method 4:
Reading the yield point at a previously set, very low shear rate
Here the shear rate, for example 1 s^{-1} or 0.1 s^{-1}, is used for evaluation. Often scientists will even select a value of 0.01 s^{-1} to approximate the state at rest.

Measuring example:
Flow curve and yield point of ketchup *(Figure 7.8)*
The yield point of a ketchup sample should be determined. A controlled-shear-stress test was carried out using ascending logarithmic steps. The flow-curve diagrams were presented on both linear and log scales in order to read the yield value as an intercept on the shear-stress axis. In the linear diagram, this value can barely be determined with the naked eye. However, on a logarithmic scale, the yield value is clearly visible as 48 Pa at a shear rate of 1 s^{-1}.

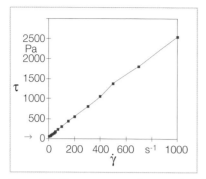 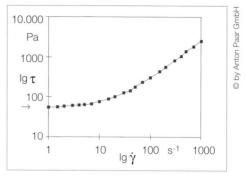

Figure 7.8: Flow curves on a linear scale (left) and on a log scale (right) used for evaluation of the yield point (indicated by the red arrow in each case) of a ketchup sample. For a visual evaluation, the log scale is much better because here the yield point can be read much more easily.

Measuring example:
Comparison of the flow curves and yield points of two coatings *(Figure 7.9)*

A comparison test was made with a **primer** C1 and a **top coating** C2. The controlled-shear-stress test was carried out using ascending logarithmic steps. The flow-curve diagrams are presented both on linear and log scales. On the linear-scale diagram, the yield point as an axis intercept of the flow curve can only - if at all - be read on the shear-stress axis with a magnifying glass.

On the log diagram, the yield values are easy to read: in this case 15 Pa for C2 and 0.2 Pa for C1, both at a shear rate of 0.01 s^{-1}. It is good for users to know that paints with yield values below 1 Pa will flow, even at rest. This means that they can even flow into the smallest gaps on the surface to be coated, which is desirable behavior for primers. Experience has shown that **dispersions with yield points of above 10 Pa** have sufficient **structural strength at rest** to show a certain physical stability against sedimentation of particles, as long as these are not too heavy. For comparison: salad dressings display similar yield values.

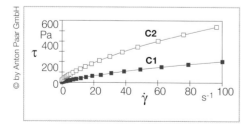 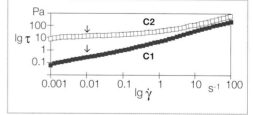

Figure 7.9: Comparison of two paints, primer C1 and top coating C2, as well as the evaluation of their yield points via their flow curves using a linear (left) and a log scale (right). The shear-stress values in the low-shear range can only be read clearly in the diagram presented on a log scale; for example, above 10 Pa for C2 and below 1 Pa for C1 at the shear rate of 0.01 s^{-1}.

8. Other flow curves and viscosity curves

Often the different flow behavior of various samples only becomes clear when their flow curves and viscosity curves are plotted together in one diagram.

8.1 Comparison of samples with and without yield point
Measuring example:
Comparison of a coating containing different rheology additives
Shown is the comparison of the flow behavior of a **water-based-emulsion paint** which has been divided into two batches. Each batch received a different additive; a **clay silicate as a gelling agent** was added to sample 1, while sample 2 was mixed with a **polymeric associative thickener**.

Conclusion: The gellant showed a good effect, especially at rest (low-shear range), while the thickener worked better in the high-shear range above $100 \, s^{-1}$.
The flow curve in the linear-scale diagram shows a yield point of 20 Pa for sample 1, determined as the intercept on the shear-stress axis. See the enlargement in the lower-right part of the diagram *(Figure 8.1, left)*. In contrast, sample 2 shows no visible axis intercept on this diagram. Therefore, with this evaluation method, it would not have any yield point. The representation as a logarithmic plot is far more descriptive. Here, the two shear stress values can be compared more clearly; for example, at the very low shear rate of $0.1 \, s^{-1}$. In this diagram, the result for sample 1 is $\tau = 18$ Pa and for sample 2 just $\tau = 0.9$ Pa. In a simplified interpretation, these values represent the **structural strength at rest**.
According to the viscosity curves, the effect of the associative thickener in sample 2 produced comparably higher values for the **high-shear viscosity**, for example at a shear rate of $1000 \, s^{-1}$ *(Figure 8.2)*. If this value is too low, **spattering** and **misting** can be expected to occur **when applying the paint with a brush or a roller**. In this case, the

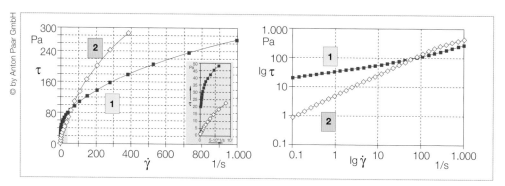

Figure 8.1: Comparison of the flow curves of two water-based coatings: sample 1 with a gellant; sample 2 with an associative thickener. Linear-scale diagram (left) and logarithmic-scale diagram (right): Additive 1 has a greater impact on the structural strength at rest in the low-shear range, while additive 2 is more effective in the range of high shear rates. The enlarged presentation on the right side of the left diagram shows both flow curves in the lower-shear-rate range.

cohesive forces of the paint's matrix are too weak to keep the droplets from spattering off the roller or brush. Towards the low shear range, the curve of sample 1 has a constantly increasing slope, while the curve of sample 2 tends to flatten out.

Measuring example:
Comparison of two sealants that have not yet hardened (Figure 8.3).
No differences in flow behavior are recognizable above a shear rate of 1 s^{-1}. However, there are basic differences between the samples at shear rates below that value: Sample 1 at rest has a firm structure because the viscosity curve approaches infinity on a constant slope. This sealing compound displays **dimensional stability** at

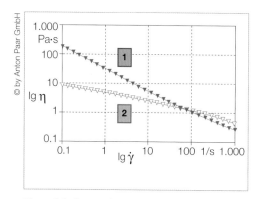

Figure 8.2: Comparison of the viscosity curves of two water-based coatings on a logarithmic scale: sample 1 with a gelling agent; sample 2 with an associative thickener. Additive 1 has a stronger effect in the low-shear range, while additive 2 is more effective in the range of high-shear viscosities.

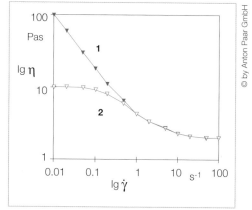

Figure 8.3: Viscosity curves of two sealants: The two sealants display the same flow behavior but differ in their behavior at rest; sample 1 without and sample 2 with the plateau of zero-shear viscosity. Sample 2 is self-levelling.

rest, even prior to the hardening process. Sample 2, on the other hand shows the plateau value of **zero-shear viscosity** at low shear rates.

In other words, sample 2 does have a high viscosity but it is still liquid and **self-levelling** at rest. It has no dimensional stability.

This measuring example shows that, in order to arrive at practical results, measurements in the low shear range (shear rates below 1 s^{-1}) are often necessary.

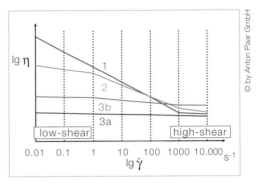

Figure 8.4: Comparison of viscosity curves to evaluate the effect of rheology additives in a water-based dispersion:
(1) with clay silicate,
(2) with cellulose derivative as a polymer solution,
(3a) untreated sample,
(3b) with an associative thickener

8.2 The effect of various rheology additives on flow behavior

Measuring example:

Comparison of water-based dispersions containing different rheology additives
(Figure 8.4)

The flow behavior of a dispersion in a non-thickened state should be compared with the flow behavoir of the same dispersion to which various rheology additives have been added.

A clay silicate was added to sample 1 as an inorganic gelling agent; sample 2 was mixed with a cellulose derivative, resulting in a polymer solution, while sample 3b contained an associative thickener.

Sample 3a was untreated dispersion; it displayed viscosity values that were too low over the entire shear-rate range; i.e., it perhaps shows **sedimentation** of particles when at rest, **uncontrolled spattering of droplets** when processed in the high-shear range as well as a **pronounced tendency to sag**.

The additives in samples 1 and 2 had a strong effect within the low-shear range, which may lead to problems when starting **to pump the dispersion**. Both additives resulted in extreme shear-thinning flow behavior, which probably results in a too-low high-shear viscosity.

Perhaps sample 3b shows the desired behavior. This sample is characterized by a balanced **low-shear viscosity**, which is nonetheless sufficient to prevent segregation of the dispersion at rest. On the other hand, it is also not too high, and thus indicates the desired behavior at the start of pumping.

Sample 3b also had a balanced **high-shear viscosity**, which thus prevented the dispersion from spattering or sagging too much when applied.

Added to that, the high-shear viscosity was not so high that this application required too much force.

8.3 Transient viscosity peak in the low-shear range with a too-short measuring-point duration

When measuring in the low-shear-range, the measuring-point duration must be long enough that the preset shear-rate has enough time to develop in the entire shear gap. If the measuring-point duration is too short, a so-called **transient viscosity peak will appear in the low-shear range of the viscosity diagram**.

Transient behavior is time-dependent behavior. Usually, a flow-curve measurement pursues the aim of obtaining a result for each measuring point that is exclusively dependent on the shear rate and not on the time of measurement.

After presetting the next-higher velocity step, the velocity gradient in the shear gap needs some time to equilibrate. This means that, at the beginning, there is no defined shear rate existing in the gap. It is only after a certain period that the flow field becomes more and more uniform until it finally reaches the desired constant shear rate in the measuring gap. This can be illustrated using the Two-Plates Model *(Figure 8.5)*. At a lower shear rate, an accordingly prolonged measuring-point duration is required.

The following rule of thumb will help: For a shear-rate range of $\dot\gamma < 1 \text{ s}^{-1}$ the measuring-point duration (t_{MP}) should correspond at least to the reciprocal shear-rate value, which means $t_{MP} \geq (1/\dot\gamma)$. Example: For $\dot\gamma = 0.1 \text{ s}^{-1}$ the measuring-point duration should be at least 10 s; and for $\dot\gamma = 0.01 \text{ s}^{-1}$ it should be at least 100 s long.

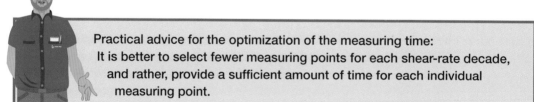

Practical advice for the optimization of the measuring time:
It is better to select fewer measuring points for each shear-rate decade, and rather, provide a sufficient amount of time for each individual measuring point.

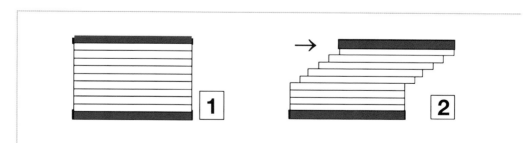

Figure 8.5: Description of transient flow behavior using the Two-Plates Model:
(1) Prior to shearing, the sample is at rest.
(2) Upon shearing, the upper part of the sample starts to flow, while the lower part still remains at rest (start-up effects).

Measuring example:
Transient viscosity peak when testing
a printing ink *(Figure 8.6)*
The viscosity curves of a highly viscous
printing ink at different measuring-point
durations t_{MP} were compared.
The test was carried out with controlled
shear rate via logarithmically ascending
steps at shear rates of between 0.01 and
$10\ s^{-1}$. For test 1, the time for each single
measuring point (i.e., the measuring point
duration) was preset as $t_{MP} = 10\ s$.
For test 2, the measuring-point
duration was set variably, descending in
logarithmic steps from 50 s at the start for
the lowest shear rate down to 2 s at the
highest shear rate. Test 3 was carried out
in the same way as test 2, except that the
measuring point-duration at the start was
prolonged to 100 s instead of 50 s.
In test 1 and 2 a transient viscosity peak

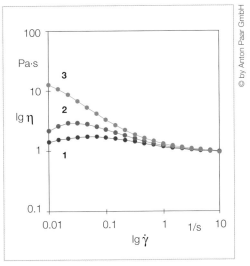

© by Anton Paar GmbH

Figure 8.6 : Viscosity curves of a printing ink. Due to
the too-short measuring-point duration, transient
viscosity peaks appear for tests 1 and 2. The peak
disappears in test 3 because here the measuring
time for each point was long enough in the low-
shear range.

was detected because the measuring-point durations in the low shear range were too
short. The occurrence of this peak is typical for this kind of measuring error. It is only
with test 3 that this peak disappears because there was a sufficient measuring-point
duration $t_{MP} = (1/0.01\ s^{-1}) = 100\ s$. Then, even at the lowest shear rate, the sample is
able to adapt to the shear conditions in the shear gap.

(3) Over time, the planar fluid layers that are closer to the moving upper plate will flow faster.
(4) After a sufficiently long measuring-point duration, all layers in the entire shear gap will flow at the same
shear rate.
The viscosity values for (2) and (3) are still dependent on the measuring time. During this period, transient
effects may be observed.

9. Time-dependent flow behavior (rotation)

For evaluating time-dependent flow behavior, shearing is kept constant. For test programs with several intervals, this applies to each individual interval.

9.1 Time-dependent structural regeneration after shearing, and thixotropic behavior

Application example:

After application, a **coating** should regenerate its structural strength within a desired period of time. **The following requirements apply to structural regeneration:**
a) not too fast in order to allow for good **levelling**,
b) not too slow in order to prevent **sagging** and to ensure a sufficient **wet-layer thickness**.

Thus, a compromise must be found between these two requirements. This compromise is balanced time-dependent behavior.

To investigate time-dependent behavior, it is recommended that a **step test** is carried out, in this case as a rotational test with three intervals.

This measurement is usually performed as a time-dependent controlled-shear-rate test *(Figure 9.1)*:

Interval (1) Very low shear to **simulate behavior at rest** at a preset low shear rate,

Interval (2) Strong shear to **simulate structural breakdown of the sample**

© by Anton Paar GmbH

Figure 9.1: Preset profile for a step test with three intervals used to evaluate the behavior of a brush coating:
(1) constant low shear rate as in the state at rest,
(2) constant high shear rate as applied in a coating process, and finally
(3) the same shear rate as in the first interval during structural regeneration at rest after application.

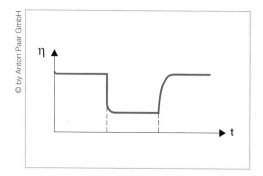

Figure 9.2: Typical result of a step test with three intervals depicted as a time-dependent viscosity function:
(1) at the beginning, high viscosity at rest,
(2) decrease in viscosity caused by structural breakdown induced by high shear,
(3) increase in viscosity by structural recovery at rest.
The example shows a material with complete regeneration of viscosity.

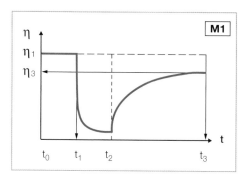

Figure 9.3: Method M1 to evaluate structural regeneration: Regeneration in the third test interval as a percentage reached at a previously defined point in time, related to the viscosity at rest at the end of the first interval.
As an example, the diagram shows 80% regeneration at time t_3.

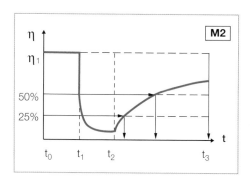

Figure 9.4: Method M2 to analyze structural regeneration: Determination of the time-points at which there is 25% and 50% regeneration in the third test interval relative to the viscosity at rest at the end of the first interval.

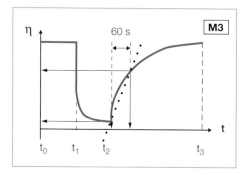

Figure 9.5: Method M3 to investigate structural regeneration: Determination of the slope of the time-dependent viscosity function during regeneration, for example within the first 60 s of the third interval.

during the coating process at a preset high shear rate, for example when applying paint with a brush or by spraying,
Interval (3) Very low shear to **simulate structural regeneration at rest** after application using the same preset low shear rate as in the first interval.

Usually, the result is presented as a time-dependent viscosity function *(Figure 9.2)*:
(1) With viscosity values almost at rest,
(2) During structural breakdown under high shear conditions,
(3) During structural regeneration almost at rest.

Definition of **thixotropic behavior**, in this case relating to viscosity (according to DIN/TR 91143-2):
Thixotropic behavior is characterized by a decrease in the values of rheological parameters such as shear viscosity against a constant, time-independent limiting value due to constant mechanical load and **the complete time-dependent recovery of the initial state upon reduction of the load**.

Correspondingly, the following applies to **rheopectic behavior** which, however, is rarely found in practical applications: Rheopectic behavior is characterized by an **increase** of the values of rheological parameters such as shear viscosity against a constant, time-independent limiting value due to constant mechanical load and the complete time-dependent recovery of the initial state upon reduction of the load.

Methods for evaluating time-dependent structural regeneration
(according to DIN/TR 91143-2):
In order to evaluate structural regeneration in the third test interval based on viscosity, the three methods M1 to M3 can be applied: The viscosity at rest at the end of the first test interval is used as the reference value for M1 and M2.
(M1) Determination of structural regeneration as a percentage of that reached at a previously defined time-point or, alternatively, at the end of the third test interval *(Figure 9.3)*.
Example for M1: After 60 s in the third test interval, regeneration reached 80% of the reference value.

(M2) Determination of the time-points for a defined regeneration as a percentage *(Figure 9.4)*
Example for M2: 25% regeneration was achieved after 10 s, and 50% regeneration after 30 s.

(M3) Slope of the time-dependent viscosity function during regeneration within a previously defined time interval *(Figure 9.5)*.
Example for M3: In the third test interval, the viscosity increases from $\eta = 200$ to 500 mPas in the period $\Delta t = 60$ s; the difference is $\Delta\eta = 300$ mPas. This results in a value for the curve slope of $(\Delta\eta / \Delta t) = (300 \text{ mPas}/60 \text{ s}) = 5 \text{ mPas/s}$.

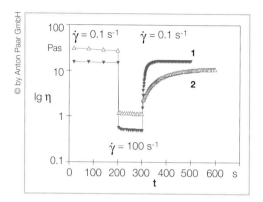

Figure 9.6: Comparison of the structural regeneration of two paints using their time-dependent viscosity curves: After shearing, the structure of paint 1 regenerates completely within 60 s, while paint 2, even after 300 s, has reached only one third of its initial viscosity at rest. Please note: The diagram is plotted on a semi-logarithmic scale.

Figure 9.7: Using a step test with three test intervals, the following situation should be simulated: First the three paints are at rest, next they are applied with high shear rates, and finally they are left alone and virtually at rest again [1].

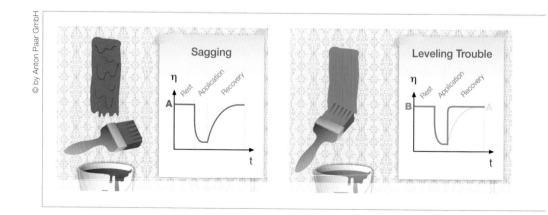

Measuring example: Levelling and sagging of coatings after application *(Figure 9.6)*
The preset shear rate in both the first and third test intervals was 0.1 s^{-1}, whereas it was 100 s^{-1} in the second interval.
Paint 1 shows **fast structural regeneration**. This means that the paint has a **low tendency to sagging** after coating, and that a **high wet-layer thickness** can be achieved. However, in the case of the structural regeneration being too fast, it is also possible that the levelling of the coating may be insufficient, with **remaining brush marks** (see also *Figure 4.7*).
Regarding paint 2, the **slower increase in viscosity** may indicate **better levelling**. On the other hand, this paint **is prone to sagging**.

Figures 9.7 and *9.8* illustrate the practical effects of time-dependent **structural regeneration after application** for three **brush paints**.
Red paint A has too slow a regeneration and it will sag too much and over too long a time.
Green paint B, on the other hand, has too quick a regeneration, resulting in insufficient levelling and the occurrence of brush marks.
Blue paint C, finally, has a **balanced regeneration time that is neither too long nor too short**. Thus, it displays the desired behavior with sufficient levelling and a negligible tendency to sagging.

Remarks regarding the evaluation of thixotropic behavior using the method of hysteresis area (or thixotropy area; *Figure 9.9*):
Hysteresis means the loop of a curve which starts and ends at the same point.

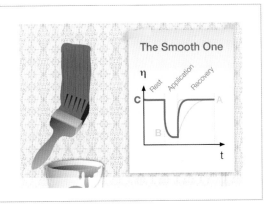

Figure 9.8: Evaluation of the structural regeneration of three paints after coating: Red paint A has too slow a regeneration and therefore is prone to sagging (left). Green paint B has a too fast regeneration and finally shows brush marks (middle). Only the blue paint C has a balanced regeneration time and delivers the desired result.

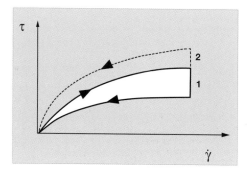

Figure 9.9: Hysteresis area between two flow curves, controlled shear rate test with upwards ramp/constant high shear phase/ downwards ramp: for (1) with decreased and for (2) with increased flow resistance caused by shearing

Three test intervals are used: An upwards ramp preset for a flow curve with increasing shear rates, a high shear phase at a constant high shear rate, and a downwards ramp for a flow curve with decreasing shear rate.

For the evaluation, the area between the upwards flow curve and the downwards flow curve is determined as the so-called hysteresis area.

The decisive disadvantage of this method is that it is **only the structural breakdown** that is evaluated, and not the subsequent structural regeneration at rest. The latter, however, is much more important for users of coatings. This is because only in this phase, practical effects such as levelling and sagging can be identified.

Conclusion: In compliance with all modern standards, **thixotropy is no longer defined as a measure for structural breakdown but rather as a measure for structural regeneration**. Therefore, using the hysteresis area for the evaluation of thixotropy is not only outdated but, according to today's definitions, wrong. Even when carrying out very simple quality control tests, you should be aware of the meaningfulness of the results obtained. Therefore the term thixotropy should no longer be used when applying the hysteresis method.

9.2 Time-dependent behavior with gel formation or curing

This test is performed under constant shear conditions either at a constant shear rate or at a constant shear stress. In most cases, tests with controlled shear rate are preferred. One disadvantage of controlled-shear-stress tests is that, with the increase in viscosity, the resulting rotational speed will continuously decrease. This would result in the deformation velocity no longer being constant. However, the latter is a decisive parameter for comparing the effects of shearing on the behavior of a sample.

The measuring temperature is kept constant, thus providing for isothermal conditions. It is recommended that **disposable measuring systems consisting of a disposable plate and a disposable dish** for single use are selected (see *Figure 3.5*). In most cases, after curing, the two parts of the PP measuring system will stick together firmly, unable to be separated or cleaned without substantial effort.

The result is usually evaluated as a time-dependent viscosity function *(Figure 9.10)*. Two time-points are of relevance here: the starting time t_s at the beginning of the curve slope indicating the **start of gel formation or a chemical curing reaction,** and the

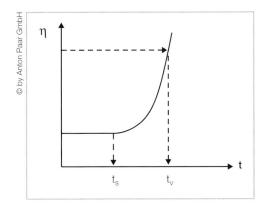

Figure 9.10: Time-dependent viscosity function of a sample with gel formation or curing: The viscosity value increases significantly after reaching time-point t_S because of the gel formation or curing reaction. A previously defined viscosity value is reached at time-point t_V.

time t_V **when a previously defined high-viscosity value has been reached**. However, with rotational tests, it is not possible to reliably provide an answer to the questions as to when a sample becomes solid and when the sample has been cured completely. This means that the entire curing process cannot be evaluated because at one point the cured mass is no longer able to flow and becomes solid. If the maximum torque of the rheometer has been exceeded, the rheometer can no longer control the preset rotational speed or shear rate. As a consequence, the speed will continuously decrease, and the viscosity will approach infinity.

This is because the viscosity value is defined by the Law of Viscosity, stating viscosity as the shear stress divided by the shear rate. In the case of curing, the shear rate would finally reach zero. This also means that the Law of Viscosity would not be applicable here.

Our recommendation: Oscillatory tests are preferred over rotational tests for evaluating gel formation and curing processes because, with oscillatory tests, materials can be examined in their solid state as well (see *Chapter 17.2***).**

Measuring example:
Curing times of a powder coating at different measuring temperatures *(Figure 9.11)*
The aim of the test was to compare the curing behavior of an epoxy-powder coating at three different temperatures under **isothermal conditions. Disposable plates were used as the measuring system** at a constant shear rate of 1 s^{-1}.
The three measuring temperatures were kept constant at T = 120 °C, next at T = 140 °C and finally at T = 160 °C.

As expected, the test showed that the reaction resin of the powder coating cures faster at higher temperatures. For each test, the user determined the **curing time** at the point when the previously defined viscosity value of η = 10,000 Pas = 10 kPas was reached. The curing times differ clearly.
The points were reached for T = 120 °C at t = 620 s, for T = 140 °C at t = 360 s, and for T = 160 °C as soon as t = 180 s.

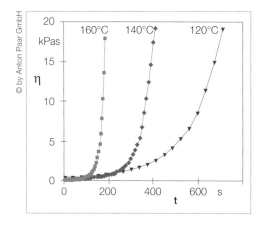

Figure 9.11: Time-dependent viscosity functions of a powder coating; isothermal tests performed at the three constant measuring temperatures of T = 120 °C, 140 °C and 160 °C. The higher the temperature, the faster the curing reaction.

© by Anton Paar GmbH

10. Temperature-dependent flow behavior (rotation)

For evaluating temperature-dependent flow behavior, shearing is kept constant. Also, a time-dependent temperature profile is preset. As a result, the function of the temperature-dependent viscosity is usually analyzed.

The **temperature gradient in the test chamber** surrounding the sample should be as small as possible. There are different methods and **devices** available for controlling the temperature:

a) Peltier elements

The Peltier effect is a thermoelectric effect. The junction between two suitable materials that are joined as layers (for example, specific metals or semi-conductors) is heated or cooled, depending on the applied voltage and the direction of current. The advantage of this method is that both high heating rates and high cooling rates can be achieved. Added to that, the size of these devices is comparably small and the investment and operating costs are relatively low. The available temperature range is usually between -40 and +200 °C.

There are two types of systems; one featuring a "**passive hood**" without temperature control and the other one with a so-called "**active hood**", where the temperature can be controlled *(Figure 10.1)*. With these **hoods**, the temperature gradient is minimal. In order to achieve precise measuring results, such hoods should be used whenever the measuring temperature differs by more than 10 °C from ambient temperature.

b) Liquid-bath temperature control

This kind of temperature control often uses water or thermo-oil-controlled thermostats;

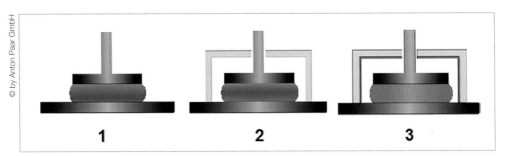

Figure 10.1: A temperature-control device has the task of generating and maintaining the temperature inside the measuring space, which contains the sample, with a temperature gradient that is as small as possible. An open system (1) is not sufficient for that. A so-called "passive hood" (2) would be a better choice but is still not optimal. This aim can only be achieved when using an "active hood" (3) that can be heated all around.

for example, for measurements that are carried out between -40 and +200 °C. The disadvantages are low heating and cooling rates and sometimes inconvenient handling of liquids in the laboratory.

c) Electric heating
This method is suitable for measurements carried out at high heating rates or at constant high temperature, for example between +30 and +400 °C.

d) Convection heating or cooling
The temperature is controlled by using an inert gas such as nitrogen; for example, for tests at temperatures between -150 °C and +600 °C. Special measuring devices and furnaces are available for testing samples such as glass, salt, and metal melts at temperatures of up to 1000 °C, and for geological tests on volcanic rocks such as basalt, even up to 1800 °C.

10.1 Temperature-dependent behavior without chemical modifications
Typical tests in this field are used for investigating **softening or melting** behavior of

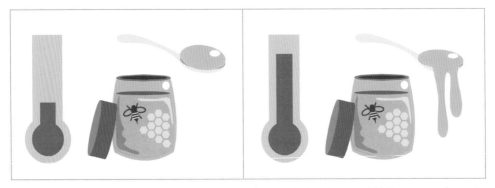

Figure 10.2: Typical temperature-dependent behavior of a sample, here honey, which becomes softer and thinner when heated [1].

samples when **heated**; or **solidification, crystallization,** or **cold gelation** when **cooled** *(Figure 10.2)*.
Practical applications of this test include evaluating the pour point of crude oils, mineral oils, lubrication oils, and motor oils; examining bitumen as a binder in road construction, even under extreme weather conditions; testing food such as chocolate for determining the crystallization temperature of cocoa butter; or characterizing cosmetic products, e.g. emulsions, in terms of their behavior at temperatures that may occur in summer or winter inside a car.

This test is carried out under constant shear conditions, either as a controlled-shear-rate test or controlled-shear-stress test.
Mostly, controlled-shear-rate tests are preferred because here the sample is always subjected to a uniform deformation velocity independent of the viscosity.
In addition, a defined temperature profile is preset, usually as a linear temperature increase over the duration of the measuring interval, for example using a time-dependent temperature gradient of 1 °C per minute *(Figure 10.3)*.
As a result, the function of temperature-dependent viscosity is usually evaluated *(Figure 10.4)*.

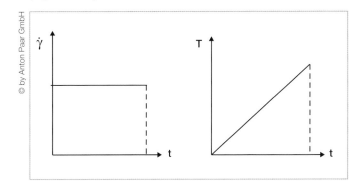

© by Anton Paar GmbH

Figure 10.3:
Example of a simultaneous preset to measure a temperature-dependent viscosity curve: at a constant shear rate and with a linear temperature increase over time.

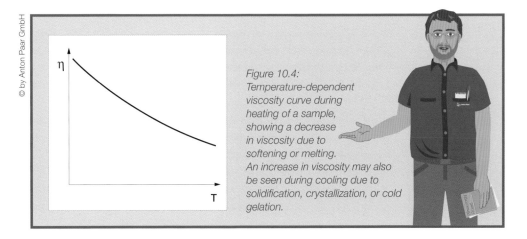

© by Anton Paar GmbH

Figure 10.4:
Temperature-dependent viscosity curve during heating of a sample, showing a decrease in viscosity due to softening or melting.
An increase in viscosity may also be seen during cooling due to solidification, crystallization, or cold gelation.

Measuring example:

Thermal behavior of a silicone oil at temperatures between -100 °C and +100 °C *(Figure 10.5)*.

The temperature-dependent behavior of a silicone oil during heating in the range of T = -100 °C to +100 °C was tested. The results showed that, despite the very broad temperature range (200 °C), the viscosity decreased by only a factor of 15. This relatively small temperature dependence of the rheological behavior is typical for silicone materials when compared, for example, to mineral oils. In a semi-logarithmic diagram, the curve of the temperature-dependent viscosity function is almost a straight line. If both

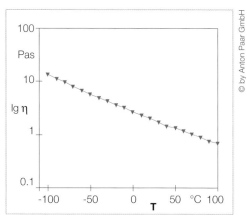

Figure 10.5: Temperature-dependent viscosity curve of a silicone oil when heated. Because this is a semi-logarithmic diagram, the curve is almost a straight line.

axes had been plotted on a linear scale, the curve would have had a bent shape with a slope decreasing from lower to higher temperature.

Measuring example:

Thermal behavior of a crude-oil sample upon cooling

The test sample was a crude oil to be cooled in the range of T = +40 °C to +10 °C. The semi-logarithmic diagram of the temperature-dependent viscosity curve shows, at T = +31.3 °C, the beginning of an increased **crystallization process of waxes and paraffins**, which are typical components of the natural product crude oil *(Figure 10.6)*. This point has been selected here as the **crystallization temperature**. The evaluation was carried out using two straight fitting lines with different slopes set along the measuring curve in the lower and upper temperature range. The two fitting lines

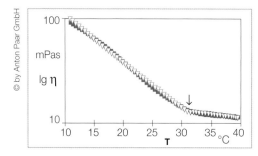

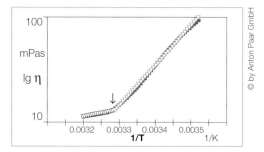

Figure 10.6: Temperature-dependent viscosity curve of a crude-oil sample during cooling, depicted on a semi-logarithmic scale. The crystallization temperature is evaluated at the bending point, here at T = +31.3 °C. Also shown are the two straight fitting lines in the lower and upper temperature range.

Figure 10.7: Temperature-dependent viscosity curve of a crude-oil sample during cooling, here shown with the reciprocal temperature in K (kelvin) on the x-axis according to the Arrhenius model. The crystallization temperature of T = 31.3 °C corresponds to 1/T = 0.00328 1/K.

intersect at this temperature point. Often the **Arrhenius model** is used for **evaluating the temperature-dependent viscosity function**. This model operates with reciprocal temperature values in K (kelvin).

The following holds: T (in K) = T (in °C) + 273.15. For example, 27 °C is equivalent to approx. 300 K. Plotting 1/T (with the unit 1/K) on the x-axis makes the respective evaluation easier when using the Arrhenius model *(Figure 10.7)*. In this case, the measuring curve is mirrored, thus showing the thermal behavior at low temperature on the right side of the diagram now. The crystallization temperature of T = 31.3 °C occurs as 1/T = 1 / (273.2 + 31.3) 1/K = 1/304.5 1/K = 0.00328 1/K.

Waxes and paraffins can cause problems when working with petrochemicals because of their crystallization. Therefore, their behavior at low temperature must be taken into consideration. Examples include fuels, lubrificants and bitumen. Some drivers of cars with diesel motors report that this phenomenon has occurred on very cold winter days, when clogged fuel filters have brought their cars to a standstill.

Measuring example:
Evaluation of the cloud point and pour point of a crude oil sample
A waxy crude oil sample was tested with cooling from T = +55 °C to +22 °C.
The measuring program had two intervals:
1) Pre-shearing: 3 minutes at T = +55 °C at a constant shear rate of 50 s^{-1}. This interval served for the simultaneous homogenization and temperature equilibration of the sample.
2) Measurement: Cooling from T = +55 °C to +22 °C with a temperature gradient of $\Delta T/\Delta t$ = 1 °C/min at a constant shear rate of 50 s^{-1}
These two temperatures (cloud point and pour point) are very important in practice and they were determined by an appropriate software program. **There are several methods available for evaluating cloud point and pour point**. This means that the method applied must be known when discussing these temperature values. The evaluation method described below uses an analysis software that calculates the most important curve points (this is performed with the help of the so-called mathematical derivative of the viscosity function with respect to temperature). Usually, a semi-logarithmic diagram is used where viscosity η is plotted on a logarithmic scale versus temperature T on a linear scale, see *Figure 10.8*.

a) The cloud point
The cloud point (CP) characterizes the point at which an oil starts to turn cloudy. At this temperature, the first effects from the crystallization of waxes or paraffins become visible. CP is read at the bending point (1) where the slope of the viscosity curve increases; in this case it is at T = 36.5 °C, where viscosity η = 11.0 mPas. This point is calculated by the analysis software (as the local maximum of the first derivative of the viscosity function).

b) The pour point (evaluation method 1)
The pour point (PP) describes the viscosity immediately before the oil starts to solidify

(thicken). If this happens, the solidification point has already been reached. This is the temperature at which crystallization of the oil has proceeded, beyond which the oil will no longer be able to flow.

PP is read at the inflection point (2) of the viscosity curve. In this case, it is at T = 32.8 °C, where viscosity η = 94.0 mPas. The inflection point is calculated by the analysis program (at the maximum of the second derivative of the viscosity function).

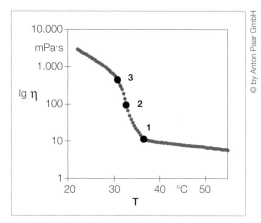

Figure 10.8: Temperature-dependent viscosity curve of a crude-oil sample during cooling from +55 °C down to +22 °C, showing the cloud point (1) at the beginning of the increase in curve slope, the pour point (2) at the inflection point (evaluation method 1) as well as the pour point (3) at the point where the curve starts to flatten (evaluation method 2).

c) The pour point (evaluation method 2)
This is an **alternative method for the determination of the pour point**. Here the temperature at the bending point (3) of the curve is determined; this is the point where the viscosity curve tends to flatten after having passed the inflection point. In this case it is at T = 30.8 °C, where viscosity η = 426 mPas. This point is also calculated by the analysis software (similar to the first bend of the curve, as the local maximum of the first derivative of the viscosity function).

Measuring example:
Comparison of the viscosity curves of two base oils at +20 °C and -40 °C
(Figure 10.9)
The shear-rate-dependent viscosity functions of two **base oils for lubricating greases** were compared: (1) a semi-synthetic oil with a **pour point** of -24 °C and (2) a fully synthetic oil with a pour point of -60 °C. The isothermal test was carried out at two constant temperatures: T = +20 °C and T =

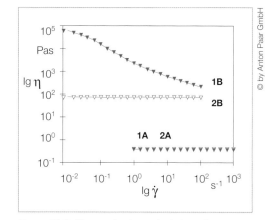

Figure 10.9: Shear-rate-dependent viscosity curves of two base oils for lubrication greases, oil 1 with a pour point of -24 °C, oil 2 with a pour point of -60 °C. At +20 °C, both oils are ideal-viscous, with the same viscosity (1A and 2A). At -40 °C, oil 1 displays inhomogeneous flow behavior (1B) while oil 2 still shows ideal-viscous flow behavior (2B).

-40 °C. At +20 °C, the two oils show ideal-viscous flow behavior, with the same viscosity value of η = 0.4 Pas (1A und 2A). At -40 °C, oil 2 is still ideal-viscous but now has a clearly increased viscosity of η = 80 Pas (2B). On the other hand, oil 1 displays irregular flow at -40 °C and has a gritty texture because the measurement took place below the pour point of this oil (1B).

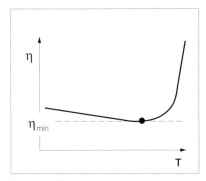

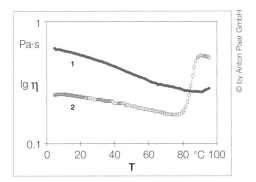

© by Anton Paar GmbH

Figure 10.10:
Temperature-dependent viscosity function during heating, with the minimum viscosity η_{min} and subsequent increase in viscosity caused by a gelation or curing process.

Figure 10.11: Temperature-dependent viscosity functions used for comparison of two ketchup samples when heated: (1) containing an unknown binding agent and (2) with starch as a binder. At T = +78 °C sample 2 starts to gelatinize.

Relating to the shear gap, this oil's texture is not uniform; it is partly still liquid and partly already frozen. This can be visualized as follows: The structure can be compared with a mixture of liquid water and solid ice - just as an icebreaker will tail behind after it has broken through the ice pack.

10.2 Temperature-dependent behavior with gel formation or curing

Typical tests in this field are aimed at investigating the **behavior during gel formation or chemical curing when a sample is heated**. This measurement is carried out under constant shear conditions, either as a controlled-shear-rate (CSR) test or a controlled-shear-stress (CSS) test.

In most cases, CSR tests are preferred. One disadvantage of CSS tests is that, with increasing viscosity, the resulting rotational speed will decrease continuosly. This would result in the deformation velocity no longer being constant. However, the latter is a decisive parameter for the comparability of the effects that shearing has on the behavior of a sample.

In addition, a defined temperature profile is preset, for example with a time-dependent temperature gradient of 1 °C/min.

For these tests, it is recommended that **disposable measuring systems consisting of a disposable plate and a disposable dish** for single use are selected (see *Figure 3.5*). In most cases, after the curing process, both parts of the PP system will stick together firmly and cannot be separated or cleaned without substantial effort.

Evaluation is carried out using a temperature-dependent viscosity curve *(Figure 10.10)*. The focus is predominantly on the evaluation of the **temperature at minimum viscosity** and the **viscosity value** at this point. **If the minimum viscosity is too high, the sample might not level** as well as desired; **if it is too low**, problems such as **edge failure** of the coating may occur.

Measuring example:
Comparison of the thermal behavior of two ketchup samples *(Figure 10.11).*

Please note: It is, in principle, not possible to evaluate an entire hardening or curing process with a rotational test because the viscosity will eventually approach infinity. Therefore, oscillatory tests are recommended for the evaluation of gel formation and curing processes because, with such tests, materials can be examined in their solid state as well *(see Chapter 18.2).*

Two ketchup samples were heated and their behavior compared. Sample 2 contained starch as a binding agent; the binder of sample 1 was not known. The tests were carried out at a constant shear rate of 60 s^{-1} each in order to reduce sedimentation of the starch granules. A cylinder system **with solvent trap was used to limit the evaporation of water**. An increase in the temperature-dependent viscosity function of sample 2 shows clearly that **starch gelation starts** at T = +78 °C.

Measuring example:
Gelation of starch at a defined temperature profile *(Figure 10.12)*
The aim of the test was to analyze the gelation process of a water-based 6% starch dispersion using a defined-temperature program.

The temperature profile consisted of three intervals:
Ramp-like heating for 15 minutes from T = +15 °C to 98 °C, 9 minutes holding time at a constant temperature of T = 98 °C, and finally ramp-like cooling for 15 minutes from 98 °C to 15 °C.
A starch measuring cell with a special stirrer geometry was used in order to generate turbulent flow so as to prevent the starch granules that have not yet thickened from settling. *Figure 2.7* shows such a starch stirrer. Furthermore, the measuring cell was **pressurized to p = 0.5 MPa (= 5 bar)** in order to prevent evaporation of water (similar to the principle of a pressure cooker at home in the kitchen).

Using the time-dependent viscosity function, the analysis software determined characteristic time-points, temperatures and viscosity values, as well as the shape of the resulting curve.

Three processing steps are important:
1) Start of starch gelation when heated,
2) Cooking behavior when held at a constant high temperature, and
3) Cold gelation when cooled to ambient temperature and below.

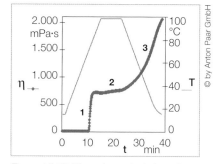

Figure 10.12: Time-dependent viscosity curve during heating and cooling of a starch dispersion, tested with a three-stage temperature program. The following processing steps can be seen:
(1) Increase in viscosity during heating caused by the gelation of the starch,
(2) Behavior when held at a constant high temperature, and
(3) cold gelation with an increase in viscosity during cooling.

© by Anton Paar GmbH

11. Viscoelastic behavior

Many materials display a mixture of viscous and elastic behavior when sheared. This is called viscoelastic behavior.

For clarification, just recall the map of **Rheology Road**, which you stroll along with Joe Flow, who explains the world of rheology and rheometry (see *Introduction* and *Figures 11.1* to *11.3*).

The most extreme materials on this road are **ideal-viscous liquids** such as water and oil on one side, and **ideal-elastic solids** such as stone and steel on the other side.

In between are the areas where **viscoelastic liquids** such as shampoos and glues and **viscoelastic solids** such as gels and rubbers are at home.

The following section deals with typical effects caused by viscoelastic behavior, with special attention paid to the elastic portion:

© by Anton Paar GmbH

Figure 11.1: Joe Flow is your guide on the way along Rheology Road

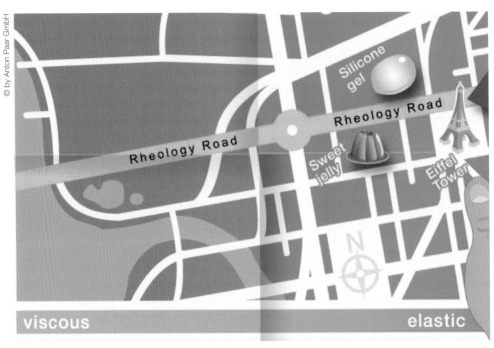

© by Anton Paar GmbH

viscous   elastic

Figure 11.2: Rheology Road runs from left to right, from low-viscosity liquids, such as water, via the district where viscoelastic materials, such as gels, are at home, and ends in the district of stiff and elastic materials, such as metals.

Figure 11.3: Here are four materials lined up as can be found on Rheology Road. From left to right: water as an ideal-viscous liquid, hair shampoo as an example of a viscoelastic liquid, followed by a viscoelastic solid, such as hand cream, and the Eiffel Tower as an example of an ideal-elastic solid made of metal [13].

Figure 11.4: Finger test for testing viscoelastic effects, such as stringiness or brittle fracturing of shampoos, creams, pastes, adhesives, lubricating greases, printing inks, bitumen or food, such as dough [9].

a) Stringiness and tack

Printing inks or pastes with too much tack accompanied by stringiness can cause problems for printing processes, for example by pulling off and separating small parts from the paper surface. Materials such as dough, lubricating greases, adhesives and bitumen display a similar behavior.

Example:

Let's do the finger test and pull some shampoo between thumb and index finger *(Figure 11.4)*. The faster you pull your fingers apart, the more pronounced the stringiness or tack.

b) Climbing up the stirrer shaft

Whenever, in a mixing process, a material climbs up the shaft **during stirring**, the mixing result inside the vessel is sub-optimal. This is known as the rod-climbing effect *(Figure 11.5)*. Rheologists also call this the **Weissenberg effect**. It was the physicist K. Weissenberg (1893 to 1976) who researched this behavior - among other things - by scientific means. This effect can be experienced in technical applications; for example, when **stirring polymer solutions and melts** or with **highly concentrated surfactant dispersions, such as dish-washing liquids and detergents, with highly filled dispersions,** and **dough**. The faster the motion, the more entangled are the polymer molecules or surfactant superstructures, and the more inflexible is the reaction of the material in the stirring vessel.

Example:

Just stir some dough (which consists amongst others of highly complex biomolecules). The faster the stirrer turns, the higher the dough moves up the stirrer shaft. **At higher speed, the elastic portion of the viscoelastic behavior increases**. Just imagine that you are standing more on the elasticity side of Rheology Road then.

Figure 11.5: One example of a viscoelastic effect can be observed when material climbs up the stirrer shaft; for example, polymer solutions such as polyisobutylene (PIB), or dough [4].

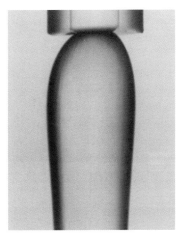

Figure 11.6: Another viscoelastic effect is die swell, which occurs when a material is extruded or flows out of a tube; for example, polymer solutions such as polyisobutylene (PIB), or when a surfactant disperson such as a liquid soap is squeezed out of a bottle [4].

c) Die swell or extrudate swell during extrusion

Die swell is a phenomenon that can occur when a material **flows out of a capillary, tube, pipe or bottle** *(Figure 11.6)*. This effect can have a strong influence on the dimensional stability of an extrudate, for example when producing PVC plastic window frames by extrusion.

Example:
Just squeeze shampoo out of a bottle, slowly at first, and then quickly. The stronger the squeezing force, the stronger the die swell. Here again, the following holds: **The elastic portion of the viscoelastic behavior will increase with higher shear and thus with the resulting higher deformation rate**.

d) Shear fracture or melt fracture during extrusion
Shear fracture or melt fracture can occur when **pastes and polymer melts** are extruded; it can result in streaks, sometimes twisted, rough or chapped surfaces and an inclusion of gas bubbles. The effects appear increasingly with higher pressure or higher flow velocity (Figure 11.7).

Example:
Just squeeze toothpaste from a tube, slowly at first, and then very quickly.

e) Surface effects such as orange peel
Orange-peel or **shark-skin** effects can occur in processes such as **film blowing** or **blow molding of hollow bodies**, for example plastic bottles. Occurrence of this effect can be anticipated when the forming process is too fast or carried out at too low a processing temperature. This often has a detrimental effect on the smoothness of the surface and on the transparency (Figures 11.8 to 11.10).

Conclusion:
It is often not sufficient to determine the viscosity alone because, in many processes, pronounced elastic effects may occur.
This mixture of viscous flow behavior and elastic deformation behavior is known as viscoelastic behavior.

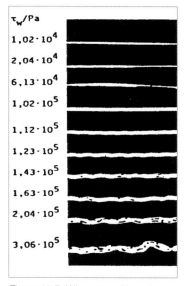

Figure 11.7: When extruding polymer melts, distinct viscoelastic effects such as surface roughness, inclusion of gas bubbles or melt fracture can often be observed with increased compression force or shear stress τ_w at the wall of the extruder nozzle (example: polystyrene, or PS), [10].

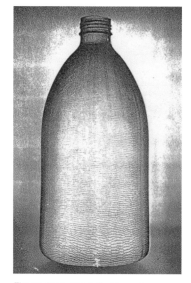

Figure 11.8: For polymer melts, viscoelastic effects can produce rough surfaces or orange-peel effects in film blowing or blow molding of hollow bodies (example: polyethylene, or PE).

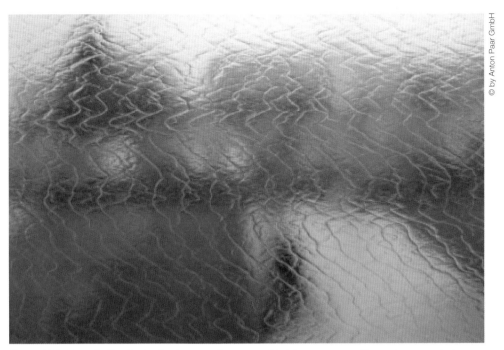

© by Anton Paar GmbH

Figure 11.9: Viscoelastic effects of polymer melts can result in inhomogeneous film surfaces, producing shark-skin effects.

© by Anton Paar GmbH

Figure 11.10: Joe Flow can be clearly seen in the left picture through a transparent film, while in the right picture, because of the shark-skin effect, you can only guess that he is there.

Often the **elastic portion** of the viscoelastic behavior is comparably **more pronounced** under the following conditions:
1) Faster movements, which mean a higher rate of deformation or shear rate, or a higher oscillation frequency
2) Lower temperatures

In both cases, the molecular networks will be less flexible and stiffer, or in other words: You are strolling along more on the elasticity side of Rheology Road. Or vice versa: The slower the motion and/or the higher the temperature, the more flexible and mobile the behavior of the molecules will be, and thus: the more you are strolling along on the viscosity side of Rheology Road.
Example:
If the dough climbs up the stirrer shaft too much, shifting the mixer into a lower gear will help, because the dough will then become more liquid.

12. Definition of terms: Shear strain or shear deformation, shear modulus, law of elasticity

The Two-Plates Model is used for the definition of the rheological parameters that are needed for a scientific description of deformation behavior *(Figure 12.1)*. The sample is subjected to shear while sandwiched between two plates, with the upper plate moving and the lower plate being stationary.

a) Shear stress

Definition: $\tau = F / A$

with shear stress τ (pronounced: *tau*), shear force F (in N) and shear area A (in m²), see *Figures 12.2* and *12.3*.

The **unit for shear stress** is $N/m^2 = $ **Pa (pascal)**.

The shear stress is calculated by the analysis software. The following data are required for the calculation: A rheometer records the shear force as a torque value at each measuring point. The torque is either preset or, if the deflection angle is the preset value, it is determined via the resistance force of the sample. The size of the shear area is also known from the measuring system used.

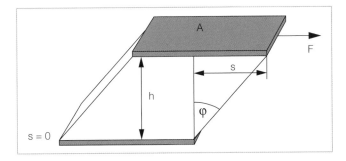

Figure 12.1:
Two-Plates Model for shear tests with shear area A, gap width h, shear force F, deflection path s, and deflection angle φ for the calculation of shear stress, and shear strain or shear deformation.

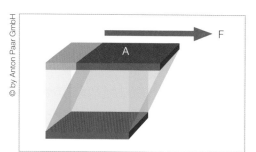

© by Anton Paar GmbH

Figure 12.2: Two-Plates Model used to define the shear stress using the parameters shear force F and shear area A of the upper, movable plate

Figure 12.3: Shear stress τ is defined as shear force F divided by shear area A

b) Shear strain or shear deformation

Definition: $\gamma = s / h$

with shear strain γ (pronounced: *gamma*), deflection path s (in m) and shear gap h (in m), see *Figures 12.4* and *12.5*.

The **unit for shear deformation** is (m/m) = 1, which means that deformation is **dimensionless. Usually**, the value is stated **as a percentage**. This is because the deformation values obtained in typical rheometer tests are very small. The following holds: 1 = 100%

The shear strain or shear deformation is calculated by the analysis software. The following data are required for the calculation: A rheometer determines the deflection path or deflection angle at each measuring point. This parameter is either preset or, if the shear force is the preset value, it is determined via the deformation of the sample. The size of the shear gap is also known for the measuring system used.

c) Shear modulus

Definition: $G = \tau / \gamma$

with shear modulus G, shear stress τ (in Pa) and shear strain or shear deformation γ (with the unit 1), see *Figure 12.6*. The plural of modulus is moduli.

This is the **Law of Elasticity** for shear tests. Often this formula is also called "Hooke's Law", after R. Hooke (1635 to 1703). In 1676, he postulated that, for solid matters,

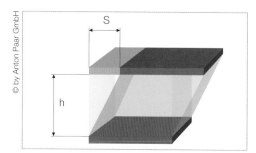

© by Anton Paar GmbH

Figure 12.4: Two-Plates Model used to define the shear strain using the parameters deflection path s of the upper, movable plate and distance h between the plates

Figure 12.5: Shear strain γ is defined as deflection path s divided by shear gap width h.

force is proportional to deformation. In fact, Hooke's law was formulated in this form, but not before the beginning of the 19th century, for example in 1807 by T. Young (1773 to 1829) and in 1827 by A. L. Cauchy (1789 to 1857).

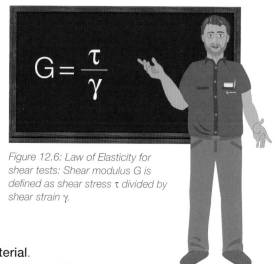

Figure 12.6: Law of Elasticity for shear tests: Shear modulus G is defined as shear stress τ divided by shear strain γ.

The **unit for shear modulus** is **Pa (pascal)**. Other units are:
1 kPa (kilo-pascal) = 1000 Pa,
1 MPa (mega-pascal) = 1000 kPa = 10^6 Pa, and 1 GPa (giga-pascal)
= 1000 MPa = 10^6 kPa = 10^9 Pa.

The higher the G value, the stiffer the material.
The Law of Elasticity can be compared with the **Law of Springs**:
F / s = C, with spring force F, deflection path s, and spring constant C, which describes the stiffness of a spring (Figure 12.7). Table 4 presents some shear modulus values. Illustrative examples for solids with different degrees of stiffness are hand creams, sweet jelly, erasers, car tires and various types of cheese (Figures 12.8 to 12.10).

Figure 12.7: The stiffness of a spring can be determined using the force that acts upon the spring and the resulting deflection path of the spring, for example for an extension spring or a compression spring [11].

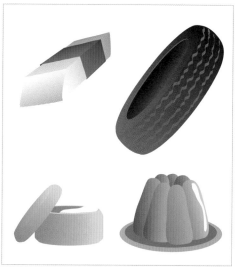

Figure 12.8: Typical viscoelastic materials with different degrees of stiffness and corresponding values of shear modulus G are hand creams (with G = approx. 100 Pa), sweet jelly (approx. 1000 Pa), erasers (approx. 1 MPa) and car tires (approx. 10 MPa)

Material	Shear modulus values (G)
Very soft gel structures (example: salad dressings)	5 to 10 Pa
Soft gel structures (example: coatings or paints)	10 to 50 Pa
Viscoelastic gel structures (dispersions, lotions, creams, ointments, pastes, cosmetics, pharmaceuticals, medical products)	50 to 5000 Pa (often 100 to 500 Pa)
Sweet jelly, dairy puddings (containing 5 / 7.5 / 10 / 15% starch)	0.1 / 0.5 / 1 / 5 kPa
Gummy bears	10 to 500 kPa
Cream cheese / soft cheese / semi-hard cheese / hard cheese / extra hard cheese	1 kPa / 10 kPa / 100 kPa / 500 kPa / 1 MPa
Soft natural rubber, erasers Unfilled and filled rubber Technical elastomers, hard rubber (e.g. car tires)	0.03 to 0.3 MPa, 1 MPa 0.3 to 5 MPa, 3 to 20 MPa 0.3 to 30 MPa, 10 to 100 MPa
Bitumen (example): at T = 0 / -10 / -30 / -50 °C	10 / 50 / 200 / 500 MPa
Thermoplastic polymers, unfilled, uncrosslinked	0.1 to 2 GPa
PVC-P (plasticized, soft, with Tg > +20 °C) PVC-U (unplasticized, hard, unfilled)	0.5 to 5 MPa 0.3 to 1 GPa
Neat resins / filled and fiber-reinforced resins used as composite materials (dependent on the orientation of fibers)	1 to 2 GPa / 2 to 12 (24) GPa
Ceramics / porcelain / marble stone / glass (window pane)	15 to 35 GPa / 25 GPa / 28 GPa / 30 GPa
Metals: aluminum (Al 99.9%) / steel	28 GPa / 80 GPa

Table 4: Overview of some shear-modulus values (at an ambient temperature, unless otherwise specified

Figure 12.9: Cheese mice testing the stiffness of different types of cheese, left picture: start of the test without any strain, right picture: final result
From left to right, the stiffness of the samples increases and, with that, the value of the shear modulus G: from cream cheese to soft, semi-hard, hard and extra hard cheese [1].

Figure 12.10: Material stiffness and shear moduli, illustrated by different types of cheese (clockwise, starting on top):
Cream cheese (G = approx. 1 kPa),
soft cheese (10 kPa),
semi-hard cheese (100 kPa),
hard cheese (500 kPa) and
extra hard cheese (1 MPa)

13. Yield point, evaluation using the deformation/shear stress diagram

A sample starts to flow only if the external forces applied are stronger than the network forces of the material's inner structure. The yield point is the value of the limiting shear stress, stated in Pa. Below the yield point, elastic deformation behavior occurs; this means that the material's structure in this region can return completely to its former shape when the stress has been removed. For determining the yield point, it is recommended that a test is performed with controlled force or controlled shear stress instead of a controlled-strain test or a controlled-shear-rate test, respectively.

Analysis of the yield point using a γ/τ diagram (deformation / shear stress) will be explained in this chapter *(Figure 13.1)*. As the values of the parameters presented in this diagram are very small, it is best to use a logarithmic scale for both axes. Here, the shear stress is preset in ascending logarithmic steps. The measurement takes place as a rotational movement with very small steps into one direction. You could say that it resembles a discontinuous rotational movement.

For samples that have a yield point, the curve function at low shear stresses and small deformations passes through a **region of linear elastic deformation** and takes on the shape of a straight line. This means that τ is proportional to γ. After exceeding the yield point, the measured values deviate from this linearity. Thus, the yield point is a limiting value, and is sometimes also called the **linearity limit**. In the subsequent flow range, the deformation increases more rapidly than the shear stress.

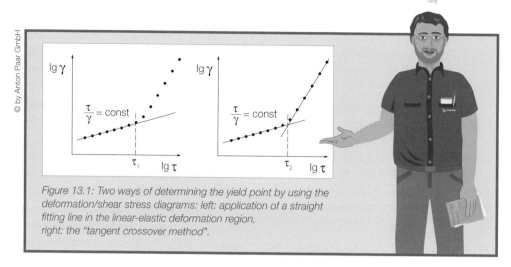

Figure 13.1: Two ways of determining the yield point by using the deformation/shear stress diagrams: left: application of a straight fitting line in the linear-elastic deformation region, right: the "tangent crossover method".

There are two methods for determining the yield point using the γ/τ diagram:

a) Method 1: Limit of the linear-elastic region

After fitting a **straight line** to the linear-elastic (LE) region, the yield point is exceeded at the point where the deformation starts to deviate from the straight line. The extent of the **acceptable maximum deviation** can be preset by the user; for example, as a tolerance band with a width of $\pm 5\ \%$. Next, the analysis software determines the corresponding τ value. Some users call the straight fitting line a "tangent", even though this term is not quite correct in this context.

b) Method 2: "Tangent crossover method"

Here, in addition to the straight line in the LE region, another **straight line** is fitted in the flow range. Finally, the value of τ at the crossover point of the two straight lines is taken as the yield point.

The following holds: **The yield point determined is not a material constant** because it always depends on the pretreatment of the sample and the measuring method, as well as on the evaluation method.

Compared to the evaluation methods based on flow curves, as described in *Chapter 7*, the methods explained in this chapter have one great advantage: Since the **yield point is considered to be a point between two regions**, the deformation behavior can be determined even before the sample starts to flow.

At first, the material is solid and its behavior is characterized by applying the Law of Elasticity - this is the LE region.

Finally, the sample flows and its behavior can then be described by the Law of Viscosity using viscosity values. The transition between the two regions can be sudden, with a sharply bent curve, or moderate, with a smoothly rounded curve. It is here in the region of viscoelastic behavior, where the elastic and the viscous portions of the material compete for dominance.

Apart from simple evaluations, as described in *Chapter 7*, other methods for the determination of the yield point are also explained in *Chapter 15.2*.

Note: Yield point and flow point
In the chapter at hand, we do not distinguish between yield point and flow point, as this is done scientifically and more precisely in *Chapter 15.2*.
The **yield point** corresponds to the shear-stress value used to determine the limit of the linear-elastic region, also called the **linearity limit**, using method 1 as described above. The **flow point** can then be compared to the shear-stress value determined by method 2 (fitting-line crossover method) as described above.

Measuring example:
Comparison of the yield points of two ketchup samples *(Figure 13.2)*.
Two ketchup samples were compared; sample 1 **without a binding agent**, and sample 2 **with starch used as a binder.** The two yield points were determined using a deformation/shear-stress diagram by fitting a straight line in the linear-elastic deformation region. The tolerance range for the maximum deviation of the measuring points from the fitted line was set to ± 10 %. As a result, the yield point of sample 1 was found to be 13.5 Pa, and 114 Pa for sample 2.

Measuring example:
Comparison of two coatings with and without a yield point *(Figure 13.3)*.
A comparison test was carried out on **primer** 1 and **top coat** 2. For the evaluation, a logarithmic γ/τ diagram and a fitted straight line in the linear-elastic deformation region

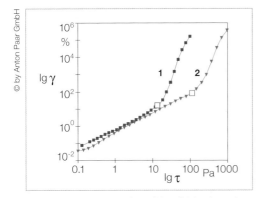

© by Anton Paar GmbH

Figure 13.2: Determination of the yield points of two ketchup samples using the deformation/shear stress diagram and the fitted straight line in the linear-elastic deformation region:
13.5 Pa for sample 1 without a binding agent and 114 Pa for sample 2 with a binder.

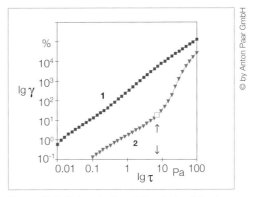

© by Anton Paar GmbH

Figure 13.3: Determination of the yield points of two paints using the deformation/shear-stress diagram, with the fitted straight line in the linear-elastic deformation region. The yield point of top coat 2 is approximately 7 Pa.
Primer 1 has no yield point because the curve does not bend; the deformation values are consistently high, thus making the paint flow even with the lowest stress applied.

were used (deviation tolerance ± 5 %). A yield point of 7.02 Pa was determined for top coat 2 at the bending point of the curve.

Primer 1 has no yield point since there is no bending point.

For sample 1, the deformation values are significantly higher, even in the region of very low shear stresses.

For example, when presetting $\tau = 0.1$ Pa, the deformation of sample 1 is $\gamma = 10$ % while for sample 2 it is merely $\gamma = 0.1$ %. In other words, primer 1 displays a deformation that is one hundred times higher, which simply means that this paint has already started to flow at this minimal stress.

14. Oscillatory tests

The Two-Plates Model can also be used for explaining oscillatory tests (Figure 14.1). A sample is sheared while sandwiched between two plates, with the upper plate moving and the lower plate remaining stationary. A push rod mounted to a driving wheel moves the upper plate back and forth parallel to the lower plate, as long as the wheel is turning. At constant rotational speed, the model operates at a correspondingly constant oscillating frequency.

Both plates are equipped with sensors. The first sensor detects the **deflection path** of the upper, movable plate. The signal is rheologically evaluated as **strain or deformation** γ. When the driving wheel moves, the strain plotted versus time results in a sine curve with the strain amplitude γ_A (Figure 14.2).

Conclusion: Parameters for oscillatory tests are usually preset in the form of a sine curve. For the Two-Plates Model, as described above, the test is a controlled sinusoidal strain test. A sine curve is determined by its amplitude (maximum deflection) and its oscillation period. The oscillation frequency is the reciprocal of the oscillation period (Figure 14.3).

The second sensor of the Two-Plates Model detects the **force** that acts upon the lower, stationary, plate. This force is required as a counter force to keep the lower plate in position. The signal is rheologically evaluated as **shear stress** τ. If the sample is not strained by too large a deformation, the resulting diagram over time is a sinusoidal curve of the shear stress with the amplitude τ_A. The two sine curves, i.e., the preset as well as the response curve, oscillate with the same frequency. However, if too large a strain were to be preset, the inner structure of the sample would be destroyed, and the resulting curve would no longer be sinusoidal.

Figure 14.1:
Oscillatory test illustrated by
the use of the Two-Plates
Model with driving wheel and
push rod for shear tests.
The deflection of the upper
plate at the angle positions
0° / 90° / 180° / 270° / 360° of
the rotating wheel is shown [1].

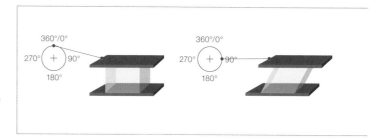

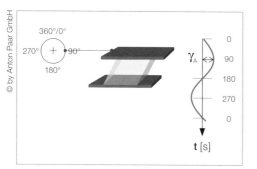

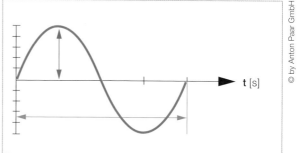

Figure 14.2: Oscillatory test using the Two-Plates Model; on the right: time-dependent strain value with the amplitude γ_A of the upper plate. Presented over the time axis, a complete sine curve is the result of a full turn of the driving wheel.

Figure 14.3: A sine curve is described by its amplitude (maximum deflection) and its oscillation period or frequency.

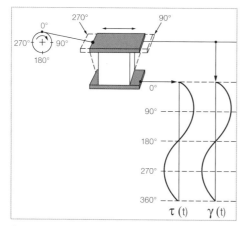

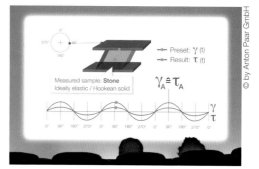

Figure 14.4: Oscillatory test with the Two-Plates Model, here for ideal-elastic behavior. There is no time lag between the time-dependent sine curves of the preset shear strain γ and the resulting shear stress τ.

Figure 14.5: With ideal-elastic behavior, the sine curves of shear strain γ and shear stress τ do not show any phase shift; the two curve functions reach the amplitude values and the zero crossings at the same time [1].

© by Anton Paar GmbH

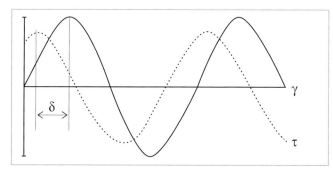

Figure 14.6:
Oscillatory test for viscoelastic behavior, presented as a sinusoidal function versus time: For example, with preset shear strain γ and resulting shear stress τ. The two curves are offset by phase shift δ.

For a completely rigid sample, such as one made of steel or stone with **ideal-elastic behavior, there is no time lag between the preset and the response sine curve** *(Figures 14.4* and *14.5).* Expressed in the language of a physicist: The curves of γ and τ are "in-phase".

Most samples show **viscoelastic behavior**. In this case, the sine curves of the preset parameter and the measuring result show **a time lag for the response signal**. This lag is called the **phase shift** δ (pronounced: *delta, Figures 14.6* and *14.7).* It is always between 0° and 90°.

The phase-shift angle cannot exceed $\delta = 90°$ because - just recall the Two-Plates Model - the rotating driving wheel would turn the upper plate in the opposite direction as soon as the angle of rotation exceeded 90°.

For the **fluid state**, the following holds: The phase shift is between 45° and 90°, thus $90° \geq \delta > 45°$. This corresponds to the left part of Rheology Road *(Figure 14.11)*. In this case, the material at rest is fluid; for example, a liquid hair shampoo. At rest it is self-levelling and has no dimensional stability.

> The following holds for the phase shift: $\delta = 0°$ for ideal-elastic deformation behavior and $\delta = 90°$ for ideal-viscous flow behavior *(Figures 14.8* to *14.10)*. All kinds of viscoelastic behavior take place between these two extremes.

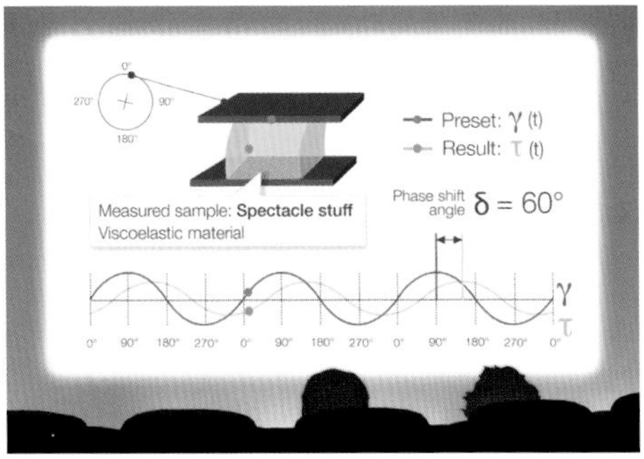

Figure 14.7: For viscoelastic behavior, the sine curves of shear strain γ and shear stress τ show a phase shift, as can be seen from the time lag between the two amplitude values [1].

Figure 14.8: Materials on Rheology Road: On the far right, for example, there is a steel cube with ideal-elastic behavior and a phase-shift angle of $\delta = 0°$. On the far left, water is flowing with an ideal-viscous behavior and $\delta = 90°$.

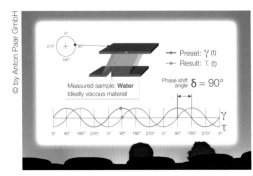

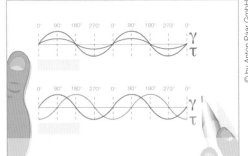

Figure 14.9: With ideal-viscous behavior, the sine curves of shear strain γ and shear stress τ show a phase shift of $\delta = 90°$ between the two amplitude values [1].

Figure 14.10: Direct comparison of ideal-elastic behavior (top) with no phase shift between the preset and response sine curves, and ideal-viscous behavior (bottom) with 90° phase shift between the two curves.

For the solid, **gel-like state**, δ is between $0°$ and $45°$: i.e., $45° > \delta \geq 0°$.
This corresponds to the right-hand side of Rheology Road *(Figure 14.12)*.
In this case, the material at rest is solid, such as pastes, gels, or other stiff, solid matter.
Examples are hand creams, sweet jelly, dairy puddings, and tire rubber.
For the purpose of illustration: Imagine that the **value of** δ corresponds to the **house number on Rheology Road**.

Raw data and rheological parameters for oscillatory tests

It is a disadvantage that the physical values determined as raw data by the rheometer are correlated to the size of the measuring system used. In contrast, the rheological parameters shear stress and shear strain, which the software requires for calculating the shear modulus, are independent of the measuring system used. *Tables 5* and *6* explain the two modes of operation for a **controlled-shear-strain** test (or controlled-shear-deformation, CSD or CD, test) and a **controlled-shear-stress** (CSS or CS) test.

In terms of units, the following holds: Torque is in Nm, where 1 Nm = 1000 mNm (milli-newton meter), strain is dimensionless, where 1 = 100 %, and deflection angle is in rad, where 1 rad = 1000 mrad (milli-rad). The angular degree (or °) is not an SI unit; this means that this unit for the angle is not useful for further calculations. It must be converted as follows: A full circle is $360°$, which corresponds to 2π rad. This means that 1 rad or $360°/2\pi$ corresponds to approximately $57°$: Thus, 1 mrad corresponds to $57°/1000 = 0.057°$ (i.e., less than $0.1°$). Since most oscillatory tests are carried out in this range, the angular deviation cannot be recognized by the observer with the naked eye.

For calculating the shear modulus, the operation mode is irrelevant because the parameters shear strain and shear stress are both available, either as a preset value or as a result of the test.

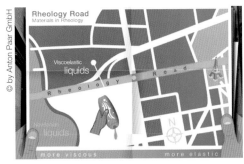

© by Anton Paar GmbH

Figure 14.11: When describing the behavior of a viscoelastic sample, which is at home on the left-hand side of Rheology Road, the viscous portion dominates over the elastic portion.
A typical example of a viscoelastic liquid is liquid hair shampoo.

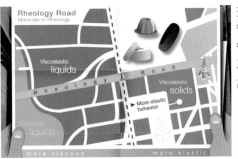

© by Anton Paar GmbH

Figure 14.12: When describing the behavior of a viscoelastic sample, which is at home on the right-hand side of Rheology Road, the elastic portion dominates over the viscous portion.
Typical examples of viscoelastic solids are hand creams, sweet jellies and rubber tires.

Oscillation with controlled shear strain	Preset test parameters	Result
Raw data of the rheometer	Deflection angle $\varphi(t)$, (in rad)	Torque $M(t)$, (in Nm) Phase shift δ (in degrees)
Rheological parameters, calculated	Strain $\gamma(t)$, (unit: 1)	Shear stress $\tau(t)$, (in Pa) Phase shift δ (in degrees)

Table 5: Oscillatory tests with controlled shear strain, raw data and rheological parameters

Oscillation with controlled shear stress	Preset test parameters	Result
Raw data of the rheometer	Torque $M(t)$, (in Nm)	Deflection angle $\varphi(t)$, (in rad) Phase shift δ (in degrees)
Rheological parameters, calculated	Shear stress $\tau(t)$, (in Pa)	Strain $\gamma(t)$, (unit: 1) Phase shift δ (in degrees)

Table 6: Oscillatory tests with controlled shear stress, raw data and rheological parameters

For converting raw data into rheological parameters, there are two conversion factors available: one is used to convert torque into shear stress, the other for converting the deflection angle into shear strain (or rotational speed into shear rate). They must be known for each measuring geometry; this is why the supplier always provides a data sheet for the individual measuring geometry.

Oscillatory tests conducted at a constant measuring temperature are also called dynamic-mechanical analysis tests (DMA). Tests carried out with varying measuring temperature are called dynamic-mechanical thermoanalysis tests (DMTA). DMA tests and DMTA tests are described as shear tests in this chapter. Furthermore, these types of tests can also be carried out as torsional tests and tensile tests (see Chapters 19 and 20) as well as in the form of bending/flexure tests and compression tests.

14.1 Complex shear modulus, storage modulus and loss modulus
a) Complex shear modulus G*
Definition of the **Law of Elasticity for oscillatory shear tests** *(Figure 14.13):*
$G^* = \tau_A / \gamma_A$
with complex shear modulus G^* (G star, in Pa), shear-stress amplitude τ_A (in Pa) and strain amplitude γ_A (dimensionless, or expressed in %).

G^* describes the entire viscoelastic behavior of a sample and is called the complex shear modulus G^*.

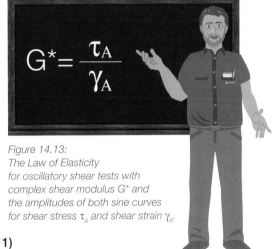

$$G^* = \frac{\tau_A}{\gamma_A}$$

Figure 14.13:
The Law of Elasticity
for oscillatory shear tests with
complex shear modulus G^* and
the amplitudes of both sine curves
for shear stress τ_A and shear strain γ_A.

Example:
Oscillatory test on two sweet jellies (Part 1)
We have cooked two sweet jellies or dairy puddings P1 and P2.
P1 contains twice the amount of starch as P2, and thus displays twice as high a structural strength. We subjected both samples to an oscillatory test in a plate/plate system (shear-gap width 1 mm) at a constant-strain amplitude and a constant frequency. For each test, the deflection angle was preset with amplitude $\varphi_A = \pm 1°$. From the rheological point of view, the rheometer controls the strain with an amplitude of $\pm\gamma_A$ (in %).

The result: Compared to P2, the rheometer determined twice as high a torque for the stiffer sample P1, with an amplitude of $\pm M_A$ (in Nm). From that, the software calculated the shear-stress amplitude as $\pm\tau_A$ (in Pa). Based on the Law of Elasticity, the software then calculated the values for the complex shear modulus G^* (in Pa) which are characteristic for the different degrees of stiffness of the samples: G^* for P1 was twice as high as G^* for P2.

Since G^* represents the entire viscoelastic behavior, our next goal is to divide this information into the two components: purely viscous and purely elastic. For this a so-called vector diagram is the method of choice.

b) Storage modulus G' and loss modulus G''
Example:
Oscillatory test on two sweet jellies (Part 2)
Up to this point, the following information about each measuring point is available for the software: First of all, it knows the value of G^*, which has been calculated based on shear strain and shear stress. The quantity of G^* can be depicted by the length of an arrow. In the language of maths, this arrow is called a vector. We select the longer G^* vector of the stiffer jelly P1, for example. The software places this vector somewhere on the drawing area *(Figure 14.14).*

Figure 14.14: Development of a vector diagram in five steps using the following parameters: (1) Vector length as the total amount of the complex shear modulus G*, (2) phase-shift angle δ defining the position of the x-axis, (3) perpendicular y-axis, (4) division of G* into the portions G' on the x-axis and (5) G'' on the y-axis.

The second piece of information that the software receives is the phase shift δ, which is the time lag between the preset and the resulting sinusoidal oscillation determined for each measuring point. In simplified terms: The analysis software now places this angle, which is always between 0° and 90°, below the G* vector. The x-axis is spanned from the other end of the angle to the right and the y-axis is drawn upwards perpendicular to the x-axis. The part of the G* value that runs along the x-axis is the elastic portion of the viscoelastic behavior presented as G' while the part of the G* vector that is projected onto the y-axis is the viscous portion G''. This means that the complete vector diagram is a presentation of G* and δ, as well as of G' and G'' *(Figure 14.15)*.

The shear storage modulus G' (G prime, in Pa) represents the elastic portion of the viscoelastic behavior, which quasi describes the solid-state behavior of the sample. Sometimes, G' is also called **elastic shear modulus**.
The shear loss modulus G'' (G double prime, in Pa) characterizes the viscous portion of the viscoelastic behavior, which can be seen as the liquid-state behavior of the sample. Sometimes, G'' is also called **viscous shear modulus**.

Viscous behavior arises from the internal friction between the components in a flowing fluid, thus between molecules and particles. This friction always goes along with the **development of frictional heat** in the sample, and consequently, with the **transformation of deformation energy into heat energy**. This part of the energy is

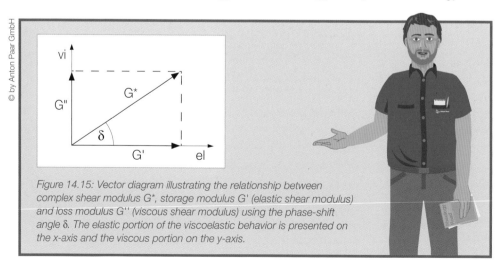

Figure 14.15: Vector diagram illustrating the relationship between complex shear modulus G*, storage modulus G' (elastic shear modulus) and loss modulus G'' (viscous shear modulus) using the phase-shift angle δ. The elastic portion of the viscoelastic behavior is presented on the x-axis and the viscous portion on the y-axis.

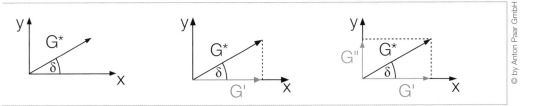

absorbed by the sample; it is used up by internal friction processes and is no longer available for the further behavior of the sample material. This **loss of energy** is also called **energy dissipation** by physicists. For scientists, this means that friction losses, energy losses and viscous behavior belong together just like cause and effect.

Elastic behavior means **reformation after release of the load.** This process requires **reset energy** and is thus only possible if this energy is available within the material as soon as it is needed. Physicists explain this as follows: During deformation, this portion of energy is stored in the deformed material; i.e., by extending and stretching the internal superstructures without overstressing the interactions and without overstretching or destroying the material. When the material is later released, this unused stored energy acts like a driving force for reforming the structure into its original shape. Thus, for physicists, stored energy and elasticity belong together just like cause and effect.

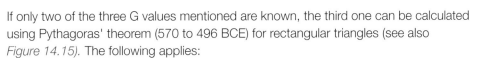

For scientists, the following holds:
Storage modulus G' represents the stored deformation energy
and loss modulus G'' characterizes the deformation energy lost
(dissipated) through internal friction when flowing.

If only two of the three G values mentioned are known, the third one can be calculated using Pythagoras' theorem (570 to 496 BCE) for rectangular triangles (see also *Figure 14.15)*. The following applies:
$G^{*\,2} = G'^{\,2} + G''^{\,2}$

Viscoelastic solids with $G' > G''$ have a higher storage modulus than loss modulus. This is due to links inside the material, for example chemical bonds or physical-chemical interactions *(Figure 14.16).*

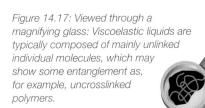

Figure 14.16: Viewed through a magnifying glass: Viscoelastic solids predominantly consist of chemically crosslinked molecules, or structures with other strong interaction forces.

Figure 14.17: Viewed through a magnifying glass: Viscoelastic liquids are typically composed of mainly unlinked individual molecules, which may show some entanglement as, for example, uncrosslinked polymers.

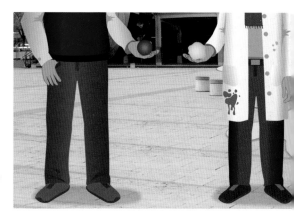

Figure 14.18:
Experiment with a rubber ball and a mass of
uncrosslinked silicone (from the left):
(1) Drop height at the beginning,
(2) Hitting the floor,
(3) The rubber ball bounces up while the silicone
mass stays on the floor in a deformed state with
subsequent levelling [1].

On the other hand, viscoelastic liquids with $G'' > G'$ have a higher loss modulus than storage modulus. The reason for this is that, in most of these materials, there are no such strong bonds between the individual molecules. Uncrosslinked polymer molecules, for example, are entangled but not chemically crosslinked *(Figure 14.17)*.

For comparison, a viscoelastic solid such as a **rubber ball** will have a dimensional stability while a viscoelastic fluid such as a **mass of uncrosslinked silicone** has no dimensional stability *(Figures 14.18* and *14.19)*.

14.2 Loss factor or damping factor
Definition of the loss factor or damping factor:
$\tan\delta = G''/ G'$
(tangent delta), unit: dimensionless or 1.
This factor describes the **ratio of the two portions of the viscoelastic behavior** *(Figure 14.20)*. The following applies (see also the vector diagram in *Figure 14.15)*:

(1) For **ideal-elastic behavior** $\delta = 0°$. There is no viscous portion. Therefore, $G'' = 0$ and with that $\tan\delta = G''/ G' = 0$.

Figure 14.19: After
hitting the floor, the
rubber ball displays
the behavior of a
viscoelastic solid with
$G' > G''$; the storage
modulus G' is larger
than the loss modulus
G''. In contrast, the
uncrosslinked silicone
is a viscoelastic liquid,
with $G'' > G'$.

$G' > G''$ $G'' > G'$

© by Anton Paar GmbH

 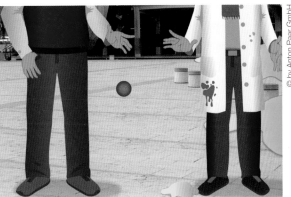

(2) For **ideal-viscous behavior** $\delta = 90°$. There is no elastic portion. Therefore, $G' = 0$ and thus the value of $\tan\delta = G''/G'$ approaches infinity because of the attempt to divide by zero.

In some diagrams, the loss factor $\tan\delta$ is plotted in addition to the curves of G' and G'', in particular, if there is a **phase transition** in the sample. This is also called the **sol/gel transition point** or simply the **gel point.**

It means that the character of the sample has changed during the measurement from the **liquid** or **sol state** to the **solid** or **gel state** and vice versa.

Examples:
Cold, solid chocolate melts in the warm mouth (and unfortunately very often in the warm hands of kids, too).
Hot polymer melt solidifies at ambient temperature, for example a hot-melt adhesive used in craft projects.
In other more illustrative words: When you reach the **middle of Rheology Road**, either from the left to the right or vice versa, the following holds for the middle of the road: $G' = G''$ or $\tan \delta = 1$ (*Figures 14.21* and *14.22*).

Example:
From water to hydrogel *(Figure 14.23)*.
Shown are five test tubes with pure water and an increasing amount of thickening agent. The following can be recognized from left to right: purely viscous behavior in the fluid state, viscoelastic behavior with the **sol/gel transition**

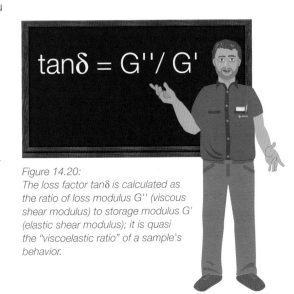

Figure 14.20:
The loss factor tanδ is calculated as the ratio of loss modulus G'' (viscous shear modulus) to storage modulus G' (elastic shear modulus); it is quasi the "viscoelastic ratio" of a sample's behavior.

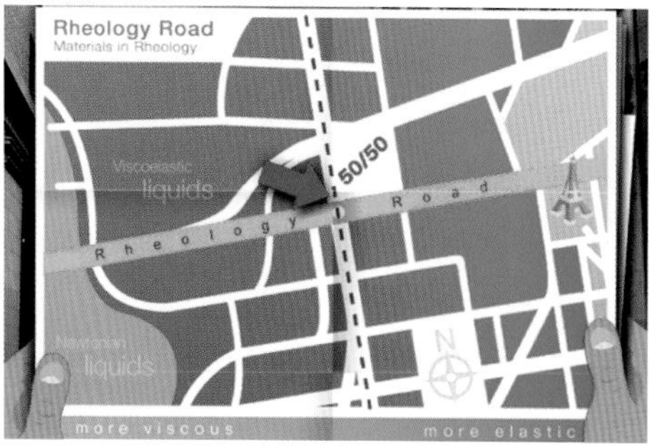

Figure 14.21: In the middle of Rheology Road, the two portions of the viscoelastic behavior are the same size; this means that the viscous and elastic portions are balanced fifty-fifty.

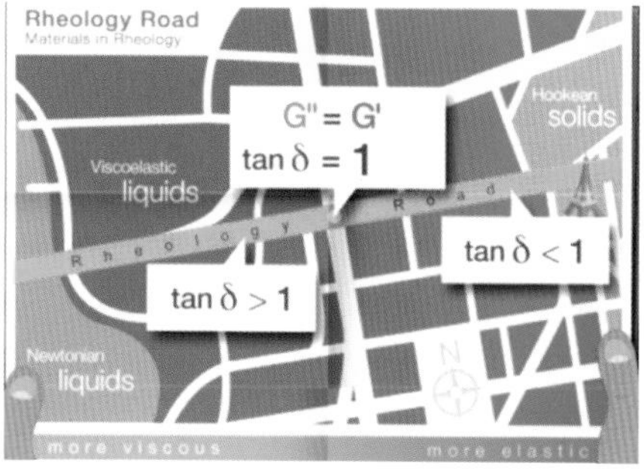

Figure 14.22: In the middle of Rheology Road, the viscous and elastic portions of the viscoelastic behavior are the same size; the following holds: $G' = G''$ or $\tan\delta = 1$.

in the center and finally purely elastic behavior in the solid state.

Expressed in rheological parameters, the five stages are:

$$G'' \gg G' \,/\, G'' > G' \,/\, G' = G'' \,/\, G' > G'' \,/\, G' \gg G'',$$

or correspondingly,

$\tan\delta \gg 1$ (or approaching infinity) $/ \tan\delta > 1 / \tan\delta = 1 / \tan\delta < 1 / \tan\delta \ll 1$ (or approaching zero).

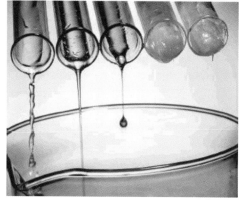

Figure 14.23: Demonstration of various kinds of behavior of water samples with increasing amounts of thickener, from the left: ideal-viscous, viscoelastic liquid, sol/gel transition, viscoelastic solid or gel-like, and ideal-elastic [14].

Usually, for practical applications, a liquid is called **ideal-viscous** if $\tan\delta > 100:1 = 100$, while a solid material is called **ideal-elastic** if $\tan\delta < 1:100 = 0.01$ Scientists are often more precise by at least one decade; they generally use the criteria $\tan\delta > 1000$ for ideal-viscous and $\tan\delta < 0.001$ for ideal-elastic behavior.

15. Amplitude sweeps

Amplitude sweeps generally aim at describing the deformation behavior of samples in the non-destructive deformation range and at determining the upper limit of this range.

Often, it is also interesting to characterize behavior that occurs if this upper limit is exceeded with increasing deformation, when the inner structure gets softer, starts to flow, or breaks down in a brittle way. These tests can be carried out on all industrial materials.

Amplitude sweeps are useful in practice to describe the behavior of dispersions, pastes, and gels; for example, for use in the food, cosmetics, pharmaceutical, and medical industries, and for coatings, sealing compounds, and lubricating greases.

For amplitude sweeps, the deflection of the measuring system is increased step-wise from one measuring point to the next while keeping the frequency at a constant value (Figure 15.1).

There are two modes of operation for presetting the deflection:
a) Strain sweep
(shear-strain-amplitude sweep, with controlled-shear deformation CSD)

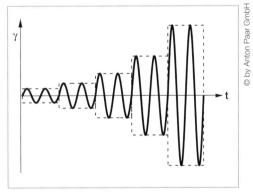

© by Anton Paar GmbH

Figure 15.1: Preset of an amplitude sweep:
Here, with controlled strain and an increase in the amplitude in five steps.
Frequency is kept constant at all five measuring points.

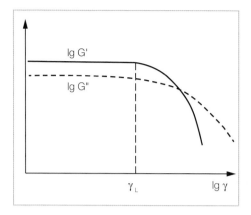 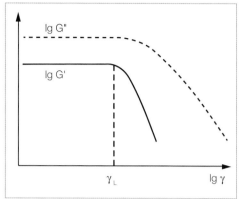

Figure 15.2: Results of two amplitude sweeps, the functions of G' and G'' show constant plateau values within the LVE region. Left: G' > G'' in the LVE region, thus the sample has a gel-like or solid structure. Right: G'' > G' in the LVE region, thus the sample is fluid.

b) Stress sweep
(shear-stress-amplitude sweep, with controlled shear stress CSS)

The frequency can be stated in one of two ways:
a) As **frequency f in Hz**; 1 Hz is one oscillation per second. The disadvantage: Hz is not an SI unit.
b) As **angular frequency ω in rad/s or in s^{-1}**, as rotational oscillation. These units are SI units. Therefore, it is recommended to work with angular frequencies. For typical amplitude sweeps, an angular frequency of $\omega = 10$ rad/s is generally used.
To convert between the two frequencies, the following holds: $\omega = 2\pi \cdot f$
with angular frequency ω in rad/s, circle constant $\pi = 3.14$ and frequency f in Hz.
Examples:
f = 10 Hz corresponds to $\omega = 62.8$ rad/s, or $\omega = 10$ rad/s corresponds to f = 1.6 Hz.

15.1 Limit of the LVE region and viscoelastic character
The measuring results of amplitude sweeps are usually presented as a diagram with strain (or shear stress) plotted on the x-axis and storage modulus G' and loss modulus G'' plotted on the y-axis; both axes on a logarithmic scale *(Figure 15.2)*.

The limit of the **linear viscoelastic region** is first determined *(abbreviated: LVE region)*. The **LVE region** indicates the range in which the test can be carried out **without destroying the structure of the sample**. It is the region depicted on the left side of the diagram, i.e. the range with the lowest strain values. For evaluation, the curve of the G' function is often preferred by users. In the LVE region, this function shows a constant value, the so-called **plateau value**.

The **limiting value of the LVE region**, also called the **linearity limit**, is determined with a ruler, an analysis software program or the data table. The linearity limit is first calculated in terms of the shear strain γ_L as a percentage. The user can either select the **tolerance range of deviation for G' around the plateau value** or leave it up to the analysis software; for example ±5% deviation (according to the standards ISO 6721-10 and EN 14770) or ±10% deviation (according to ASTM D7175 and DIN 51810-2).

In addition, the values of G' and G'' in the LVE region are also often evaluated. This indicates the **viscoelastic character** of the sample. If G' > G'', then the sample shows a **gel-like or solid structure**, and can be termed **a viscoelastic solid material**. However, if G'' > G', the sample displays a **fluid structure**, and can be termed **a viscoelastic liquid**. Of course, this counts only for the measuring conditions applied, which means for the preset (angular) frequency.

In general, the following holds:
When examining an unknown sample by an oscillatory test, an amplitude sweep must first be carried out in order to determine the limit of the LVE region.

For all subsequent oscillatory tests, it is usually required that the measurements are carried out at strain or stress levels within the LVE region.

Measuring example:
Amplitude sweep of a polymer melt *(Figure 15.3)*
When measured at T = 180 °C and at a constant angular frequency of ω = 10 rad/s, this polymer melt **with G'' > G'** shows a fluid state across the entire deformation range. Thus, under these measuring conditions, it is a **viscoelastic liquid**. The limit of the LVE region is at γ_L = 10 % (= 0.1). The plateau values in the LVE region are G' = 10,000 Pa = 10 kPa, and G'' = 15,000 Pa = 15 kPa.

Measuring example:
Amplitude sweep of a non-hardened, pasty sealant *(Figure 15.4)*
Measured at T = +25 °C and ω = 10 rad/s, this sealant shows G' > G'' within the LVE region, and thus, in this strain range it is a pasty, **viscoelastic solid**.
The limit of the LVE region determined by the analysis software is γ_L = 0.026 % (= 2.6 · 10⁻⁴).

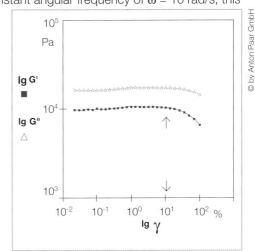

© by Anton Paar GmbH

Figure 15.3: Amplitude sweep of a polymer melt (polyethylene, PE) at an angular frequency of ω = 10 rad/s: The limit of the LVE region occurs at a strain of γ = 10 %. Within the LVE region (and also outside of it) G'' is greater than G'. The viscoelastic sample is liquid.

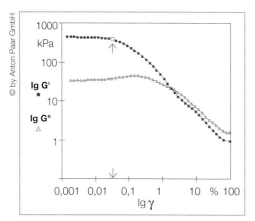

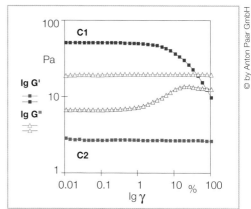

© by Anton Paar GmbH

Figure 15.4: Amplitude sweep of a pasty sealant at ω = 10 rad/s: The limit of the LVE region is at γ = 0.026 %. Within the LVE region, G' > G''. Here, the viscoelastic sample is in a solid state.

Figure 15.5: Amplitude sweeps for comparison of two cosmetic products at ω = 10 rad/s. While gel C1 shows a solid structure with G' > G'' in the LVE region, fluid C2 displays G'' > G' within the entire strain range.

Often, the LVE region of **highly filled dispersions** is more than a hundred times narrower than that of unfilled polymer melts. In the LVE region, the plateau values are G' = 450 kPa (almost 0.5 MPa, which means almost half as stiff as a rubber eraser) and G'' = 30 kPa (see also EN 17408).

Measuring example:
Amplitude sweeps for comparison of two cosmetic products *(Figure 15.5)*
The rheological behavior of gel C1 and fluid C2 are to be described. Measurement parameters are T = +23 °C and ω = 10 rad/s. The two samples differ clearly: Within the LVE region, gel C1 with G' = 50 Pa and G'' = 7 Pa is solid because G' > G''; the linearity limit of the LVE region is as low as γ_L = 1%. In contrast, sample C2 displays liquid behavior across the entire strain range, with G'' = 20 Pa and G' = 3 Pa, thus G'' > G'.

Measuring example:
Amplitude sweeps for comparison of two spray coatings *(Figure 15.6)*
After application, two spray coatings (SC) developed different levelling behavior. Spray coating SC1 showed **poor levelling**, whereas spray coating SC2 could be applied without any levelling problems. With measurement parameters T = +25 °C and ω = 10 rad/s, the limit of the LVE region for both samples is approximately γ_L = 5 %. The two samples differ clearly in the LVE region: For SC1, G' is greater than G'', but for SC2, G'' is greater than G'. Even at a very low strain, SC2 is a viscoelastic liquid with G'' = approximately 3 Pa and G' = approximately 2 Pa. In contrast, SC1 is in a solid state, despite its very low structural strength, which is reflected in the values of G' and G'' (approximately 4 Pa and 3 Pa, respectively).
The two spray coats do not differ significantly in their G'' value across the entire measuring range. This was confirmed by **information provided by the user, stating**

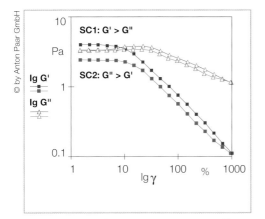

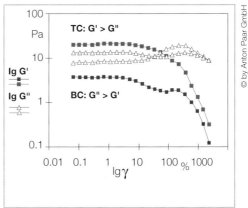

Figure 15.6: Amplitude sweeps at ω = 10 rad/s for comparison of two spray coats. The different viscoelastic characters become evident because of the differences displayed within the LVE region: For SC1, with G' > G'', the elastic behavior dominates slightly, whereas SC2, with G'' > G', is liquid.

Figure 15.7: Amplitude sweeps at ω = 10 rad/s for comparison of two brush paints. Base coat BC, with G'' > G', displays fluid behavior in the LVE region, whereas top coat TC with G' > G'' has a weak, but solid structure.

that no significant difference was found between the two spray coats in rotational viscosity tests conducted within a shear-rate range of 0.01 to 1000 s⁻¹. Despite the fact that both spray coats were evaluated as having low viscosity, they clearly differ in their elastic behavior.

> Conclusion:
> **Oscillatory tests may also be useful for evaluating low-viscosity liquids, which may show viscosity values as low as below 100 mPas when flowing.**

Measuring example:
Amplitude sweeps for comparison of two brush paints *(Figure 15.7)*
The behavior of two paints, **base coat** BC (primer) and **top coat** TC, was compared. Measured at T = +23 °C and ω = 10 rad/s, the limit of the LVE range for both samples is at approximately 5% strain. The two samples differ clearly in the LVE region: For BC, G'' > G', but for TC, G' > G''. BC is a viscoelastic liquid with G'' = 12 Pa and G' = 4 Pa. In contrast, TC has a solid consistency with a structural strength of G' = 20 Pa and G'' = 8 Pa. The G' values in the LVE region (20 Pa and 4 Pa) differ by far more than the G'' values (12 Pa and 8 Pa)..
Base coats are often developed to show a dominating G'' value in the LVE region, so that they are then able to flow continuously even if nearly at rest, thus filling all uneven parts of the material to be painted, and providing a smooth surface for the subsequent top coat.

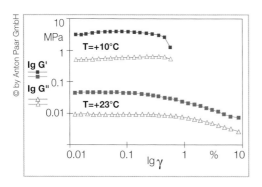

Figure 15.8: Amplitude sweep of a butter sample at T = +10 °C and +23 °C, and ω = 10 rad/s. At both temperatures, G' is greater than G'' which indicates a solid structure. At T = +10 °C, a sharp drop in G' occurs upon leaving the LVE region, indicating brittle fracturing.

Top coats, on the other hand, **often are prepared to have a dominating G' in the LVE region** by incorporating a weak, but consistent three-dimensional network of forces when the material is at rest, in order to prevent settling of pigment particles. This consistency can be described as a very **weak gel structure**. Such a property cannot be detected by rotational tests, because the elastic portion is basically not determined in such tests.

Measuring example:
Amplitude sweeps of butter at different temperatures *(Figure 15.8)*
The behavior of butter at two temperatures was compared: T = +10 °C (directly taken from the fridge) and T = +23 °C (ambient temperature). The test was carried out using a plate/plate system with a measuring gap of H = 1 mm, and at an angular frequency of ω = 10 rad/s.
In the LVE region, the stiffness of the samples differed by a factor of 100 in the G' values (5 MPa at T = +10 °C and 0.05 MPa at T = +23 °C). This means that the force needed to deform the cold butter, for example when cutting, is one hundred times greater than for the warmer butter. Or in other words: When applying the same force, the deformation of the cold butter is one hundredth that of the warmer butter.

Another difference can be seen at the limit of the LVE region by looking at the shape of the G' curve. At a strain value of approximately 0.5%, the G' curve of the cold butter drops sharply, thus indicating **brittle fracturing**. This explains why cold butter shows poor **spreadability**. In contrast, the structural strength of the butter at ambient temperature decreases only very slowly after the limit of the LVE region is exceeded. Therefore, it can be spread more easily.

Calculation according to the definition of shear strain:
γ = s/h = 10 μm / 1000 μm = 0.01 = 1 %. This means that at γ = 0.1 % or 0.01 %, the deflection path at the edge of the plate is merely s = ± 1 μm or ± 0.1 μm. This is invisible to the naked eye but is no problem for the control of a modern air-bearing rheometer.

> Remark:
> **In a PP geometry with a plate distance of H = 1 mm (= 1000 μm), at the edge of the movable plate a strain amplitude of γ = 1 % is equal to a deflection of only s = ± 10 μm.**

Measuring example:
Amplitude sweep to determine the gel strength of four gels with different starch contents *(Figure 15.9)*

The gel strength of four water-based gels with different starch contents was determined. Measurement parameters were T = +23 °C and ω = 10 rad/s.

Firstly, to be called a gel structure at all, the samples must meet the following conditions for the LVE region:

G' > G'' or, in other words, the loss factor $\tan\delta$ = G'' / G' < 1. This requirement was met.

The **structural strengths or gel strengths were determined as G' values in the LVE region** for the following starch contents (in weight-%): G' = 130 Pa at 5 wt% starch / 450 Pa at 7.5 wt% / 1500 Pa at 10 wt% / 6000 Pa at 15 wt%.

Measuring example:
Amplitude sweep for comparison of a native and a modified corn-starch gel
(Figure 15.10).

The behavior of gel S1 made with native corn starch and gel S2 made with modified corn starch was compared.

Both gels are used as **binders for dairy products such as yoghurt**.

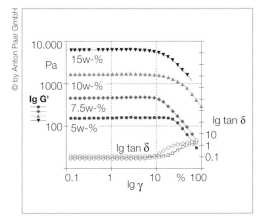

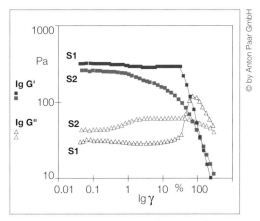

Figure 15.9: Amplitude sweeps for comparison of four gels with different amounts of binding agent in water at T = +23 °C and ω = 10 rad/s. Within the LVE region, all four samples show a gel-like state, with $\tan\delta$ = G'' / G' < 1.
Gel strength, here indicated as the G' value within the LVE region, increases with an increasing amount of binding agent.

Figure 15.10: Amplitude sweeps for comparison of two corn-starch gels: S1 contains native corn starch, gel S2 modified corn starch. S1 shows brittle fracturing; the distinct peak of the G'' curve indicates formation of micro cracks prior to the breakdown of the material's structure. For S1, the crossover point G' = G'' and the G'' maximum meet at one point.

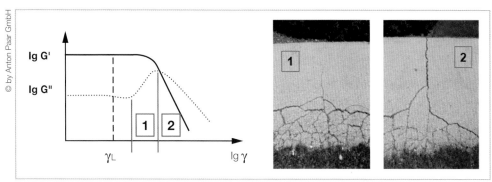

Figure 15.11: Left: Amplitude sweep of a gel with a pronounced G'' maximum.
Within zone (1) only micro cracks occur before the curve's maximum is reached. Here it is still G' > G''
(solid state). After the maximum is exceeded, in zone (2), a macro crack develops throughout the sample
up to the crossover point G' = G''; after that, G'' > G' (fluid state).
Right: Illustration of both zones with the example of cracks on a sidewalk:
(1) micro cracks that do not extend throughout the entire material;
(2) a macro crack going right through the material can be seen.

Sample S2 showed **creamier texture** when stirred, **better spoonability**, and was easier **to dose** than sample 1.

Measurement parameters were $T = +23\,°C$ and $\omega = 10$ rad/s.

Evaluation of the G' curves:

Starting from almost the same initial value in the LVE region, the curve of S1 shows a sharp downturn at $\gamma = 20\%$; i.e., the limit of the LVE region, thus indicating **brittle fracturing behavior**. This means that gel S1 under shear does not break homogeneously but rather into larger pieces. This explains the non-creamy behavior of S1.

In contrast, the curve of the G' function of S2 drops continuously after leaving the LVE region, thus indicating a gradual breakdown of the superstructure. This explains the **creamy behavior** of S2. In practice, **G' values in the LVE region** represent the **stiffness of the sample** or the **gel strength**.

Evaluation of the G'' curves:

Following an almost constant value in the LVE region for gel S1, the curve rises sharply until, after reaching a distinct peak (maximum), the curve again drops steeply. **The values of the loss modulus G'' describe the portion of the deformation energy that is lost by internal friction during shearing**. Before the breakdown of the gel has reached the point where it finally starts to flow, it is only at first that a few individual bonds in the network of forces rupture, while the entire surrounding material still keeps firmly together. This means that G' still dominates over G'' throughout the entire sample. At first, **micro cracks** start to develop. **Deformation energy is lost** because the broken, freely movable bridge fragments around the micro cracks, which are no longer integrated within the network, start to show **internal viscous friction** and thus convert deformation energy into friction heat.

When the individual micro cracks grow further, they eventually form a continous **macro crack** that runs through the entire sample, or the entire shear gap of the measuring system. If this happens, the viscous behavior of the sample dominates and the entire material will start to flow. After exceeding this point, G'' is greater than G', because the crossover point G' = G'' has been exceeded. Often the crossover point and the G'' maximum are very close, in fact they frequently appear at the same deformation value. The shape of the G'' curve at the point where it leaves the LVE region can be used to distinguish **the behavior of gels**: the maximum for gel S2 is less pronounced than that for S1, and the transition of S2 from the solid state at rest to flowing is less sharp, as can also be seen from the shape of the G'' curve.

If, in the LVE region, G' is greater than G'', and if the G'' curve has a distinct maximum at a higher strain value, the following can be stated:

1) At the beginning of the test, the **superstructure formed a consistent, three-dimensional network**.

2) The breakdown of the structure started with some micro cracks, although at that time the elastic portion of the viscoelastic behavior still prevailed (region 1 in *Figure 15.11*). Therefore, the process of structural breakdown took place with some delay.

As the strain increased, a **macro crack** finally ruptured the entire sample. Only then did the viscous portion of the viscoelastic behavior prevail (region 2 in *Figure 15.11*).

15.2 Yield point and flow point

Amplitude sweeps can also be used for determining the yield point and the flow point. No matter whether the test was performed as a strain sweep (with controlled shear deformation) or a stress sweep (with controlled shear stress), the following values are determined by either using the data table or a diagram with the shear stress τ plotted on the x-axis *(Figure 15.12)*:

1) **The yield point** τ_y or **yield stress**, is the value of the shear stress at the limit of the LVE region. The verb "to yield" in this context means to give way or to soften, for example under shear. This point is also called the **linearity limit of shear stress** (τ_L) .

2) **The flow point** τ_f or **flow stress**, is the value of the shear stress **at the crossover point G' = G''**. This point is also called the the shear stress at the crossover point (τ_{co}). At higher shear, the viscous portion will dominate and the sample flows. Both values are dependent on the measuring conditions; for example, on the preset (angular) frequency.

In the region between yield point and flow point, G' > G''. Within this **yield zone**, the initial structural strength of the LVE region has already decreased, but the sample still predominantly displays the properties of solid matter or a gel.

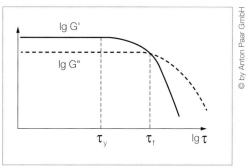

© by Anton Paar GmbH

Figure 15.12: Amplitude sweep, presented with shear stress τ plotted on the x-axis, showing the yield point τ_y at the limit of the LVE region and the flow point τ_f at the crossover point G' = G''.

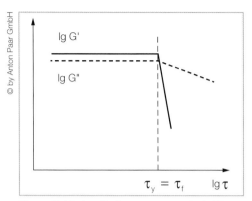

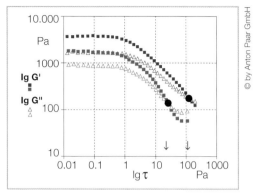

Figure 15.13: Amplitude sweep presented with shear stress τ plotted on the x-axis. If brittle fracturing occurs, yield point τ_y and flow point τ_f have the same value.

Figure 15.14: Amplitude sweeps at ω = 10 rad/s for comparison of two toothpastes. The two toothpastes have almost the same yield point at 0.5 Pa; however, their flow points differ significantly, with 25 Pa and 125 Pa.

For evaluation of the **transition behavior from the LVE region to the state of flow**, the **flow transition index** τ_f / τ_y can be calculated. If $\tau_f = \tau_y$ then this index has the value 1. The more closely this ratio approaches 1, the higher is the tendency of the sample to **brittle fracturing** *(Figure 15.13)*.

Measuring example:
Amplitude sweeps for comparison of two toothpastes *(Figure15.14)*.
In a consumer test, a toothpaste producer discovered that squeezing two different toothpastes out of the tube requires different degrees of force. Stress sweeps with a rheometer in the laboratory at T = +23 °C and ω = 10 rad/s showed that both toothpastes had a **yield point** of τ_y = 0.5 Pa; therefore, there is no significant difference between the two products. However, when evaluating the **flow points** τ_f, the values of 125 Pa and 24.9 Pa differ by a factor of five. This example shows unmistakably that the flow point and not the yield point should be used for evaluating the **squeezing force**.

Measuring example:
Amplitude sweeps for determining the flow points of lubricating greases
(Figure 15.15).
Usually, the consistency of a lubricating grease is evaluated according to the NLGI classification *(National Lubricating Grease Institute, USA)*. The standard test method is the cone penetration test, in which a

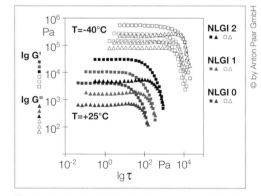

Figure 15.15: Amplitude sweep at ω = 10 rad/s for comparing three lubricating greases of consistency classes NLGI 0 (very soft), NLGI 1 (soft) and NLGI 2 (solid). The lower curves of the three greases shown were measured at T = +25 °C, and the upper curves at T = -40 °C. The flow points were each determined at their crossover point G' = G''.

Lubricating grease class	T = +25 °C	T = -40 °C
NLGI 0	100 Pa	5 kPa
NLGI 1	200 Pa	7 kPa
NLGI 2	400 Pa	10 kPa

cone is placed on top of the sample. The weight of the cone will cause it to penetrate the grease until it reaches a certain depth after a defined time. The stiffer the lubricating grease, the higher is the number of the NLGI class.

According to DIN 51810-2, the flow point of lubricating grease is determined in a strain sweep at the crossover point G' = G''. The test is conducted at an angular frequency of ω = 10 rad/s and at the two measuring temperatures T = +25 °C and -40 °C. Despite the fact that such amplitude sweeps are strain controlled, they are presented versus the shear stress. The example shows three lubricating greases of the classes NLGI 0, NLGI 1 and NLGI 2, each measured at T = +25 °C and T = -40 °C. The flow points determined for these samples are given in the table.

The controlled-strain test was preferred over the controlled-shear-stress test because the first test mode provides significantly better reproducibility of results outside the LVE region. This has been demonstrated in numerous round-robin tests conducted on behalf of the respective DIN Working Group. The reason for this is that, **with controlled strain, the change in deformation is conducted in controlled steps** via the deflection path of the measuring system, **even during the breakdown of the sample's structure.**

In contrast, when applying controlled shear stress, the structure responds to the acting shear force, which may result in an extremely large deformation with sometimes sudden and therefore inhomogeneous deformation behavior - referred to as the shear gap - or it may lead to an abrupt breakdown of the sample's structure.

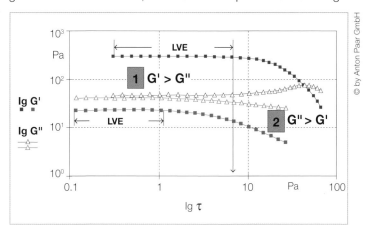

Figure 15.16: Amplitude sweeps at ω = 10 rad/s for comparing two dispersions containing different additives. Sample 1 within the LVE region shows G' > G'', yield point at 7 Pa and flow point at 42 Pa.
For sample 2 in the LVE region, G'' > G' and the yield point is at 1.5 Pa. There is no flow point because the sample is liquid across the entire measuring range.

Measuring example: Amplitude sweeps for comparing dispersions containing different rheology additives (Figure 15.16)

A **water-based solution** was divided between two containers. Additive 1, a **clay silicate, was added as a gellant to the first container**. Additive 2, an **associative thickener, was added to the second container**. Measurement parameters were $T = +23\ °C$ and $\omega = 10$ rad/s.

The evaluation showed: The dispersion containing additive 1 has a gel-like solid texture in the LVE region, with $G' > G''$, a yield point of $\tau_y = 6.9$ Pa and a flow point of $\tau_f = 42$ Pa.

In contrast, the dispersion with additive 2 behaves like a liquid with no dimensional stability in the LVE region, since $G'' > G'$. Here, the yield point is $\tau_y = 1.5$ Pa. **There is no flow point because there is no crossover point $G'' = G'$**. This applies for elastic shear-softening and viscous shear-thinning behavior; i.e., it occurs if both G' and G'' decrease with increasing strain or shear stress.

Conclusion:
If a sample shows $G'' > G'$ in the LVE region, and therefore the character of a fluid, it may have a yield point but not a flow point because it is always liquid.

16. Frequency sweeps

Frequency sweeps generally serve the purpose of describing the time-dependent behavior of a sample in the non-destructive deformation range. High frequencies are used to simulate fast motion on short timescales, whereas low frequencies simulate slow motion on long timescales or at rest. In practice, frequency sweeps are proven methods for gathering information on the behavior and inner structure of polymers as well as on the long-term stability of dispersions.

In this context, the process of describing a sample's structure often starts with the following questions: Does the polymer consist of uncrosslinked molecules or does it have a three-dimensionally bonded (crosslinked) chemical network? Is the material at rest capable of flowing, or is it dimensionally stable with a solid consistency? Is a dispersion physically stable, and will it withstand segregation phenomena such as sedimentation? In frequency sweeps (Figure 16.1), the oscillation frequency is increased or decreased step-wise from one measuring point to the next while keeping the amplitude constant.

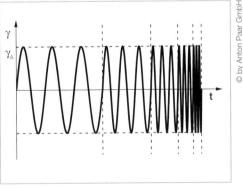

© by Anton Paar GmbH

Figure 16.1: Preset of a frequency sweep, here with controlled shear strain and an increase or decrease in frequency in five steps. The strain amplitude γ_A is kept constant over all five measuring points.

Many users prefer the method of measuring from maximum to minimum frequency as this often results in a shorter testing period due to a shorter adjustment time of the controller. The same result is obtained for either method if, on the one hand, the measurement takes place within the LVE region and if, on the other hand, the sample shows no change during the test period.

There are two modes of operation for presetting the deflection:
a) Controlled strain (or controlled shear deformation CSD)
b) Controlled shear stress (CSS)

The precondition is that the selected shear-strain or shear-stress amplitude is within the LVE region. **This means that the limit of the LVE region must first be determined in an amplitude sweep.**

As explained previously for amplitude sweeps, frequencies can be stated in one of two ways: As **frequency f in Hz** or as **angular frequency ω in rad/s or in s^{-1}**.
It is advisable to work with angular frequencies because there are SI units available. To convert between the two frequencies, the following holds, with circle constant $\pi = 3.14$: ω (in rad/s) = $2\pi \cdot$ f (in Hz).

The results of frequency sweeps are usually presented in a diagram with the (angular) frequency plotted on the x-axis and storage modulus G' (elastic shear modulus) and loss modulus G'' (viscous shear modulus) plotted on the y-axis, with both axes on a logarithmic scale.

16.1 Uncrosslinked polymers
Measuring example:
Frequency sweep of an uncrosslinked polymer *(Figure 16.2)*.
A **silicone** (PDMS, polydimethyl siloxane) was subjected to a frequency sweep at a measuring temperature of T = +23 °C and a strain of γ = 10 %. Prior to the test, it was confirmed by an amplitude sweep that the amplitude value selected was within the LVE region. The following behavior is **typical for an uncrosslinked polymer**: In

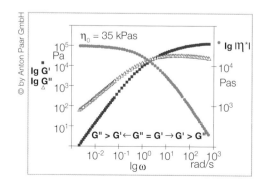

Figure 16.2: Frequency sweep of an uncrosslinked silicone (PDMS) at a strain of γ = 10 %, showing the functions of storage modulus G' and loss modulus G'', as well as the crossover point G' = G'' at ω = 4 rad/s. In addition, the function of the complex viscosity |η^*| with the plateau value of the zero-shear viscosity η_0 = 35 kPas is shown.

the lower frequency range, G'' > G' with predominantly viscous behavior; in the upper frequency range, G' > G'' with prevailing elastic properties. Thus, in between, there is the **crossover point G' = G''**.

Evaluation of uncrosslinked polymers:

1) The value of the angular frequency ω_{co} is determined at the crossover point G' = G'' (co is the abbreviation of crossover point). The position of the crossover point G' = G'' depends on the **average molar mass M of the polymer**: If the crossover point occurs at a lower frequency, then the molar mass is relatively higher *(Figure 16.3)*.

Example:

If the crossover point of one sample appeared at the end of arrow M1 and the crossover point of a second sample at the end of arrow M2, then the molar mass M1 of the first polymer would be higher than the molar mass M2 of the second sample. Therefore, in this case, M1 > M2. Instead of using ω_{co} (in rad/s or s^{-1}), its inverse value is often calculated as **relaxation time** λ (in s). The following holds: $\lambda = 1/\omega_{co}$

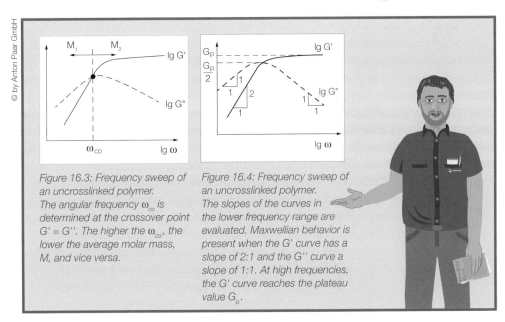

Figure 16.3: Frequency sweep of an uncrosslinked polymer. The angular frequency ω_{co} is determined at the crossover point G' = G''. The higher the ω_{co}, the lower the average molar mass, M, and vice versa.

Figure 16.4: Frequency sweep of an uncrosslinked polymer. The slopes of the curves in the lower frequency range are evaluated. Maxwellian behavior is present when the G' curve has a slope of 2:1 and the G'' curve a slope of 1:1. At high frequencies, the G' curve reaches the plateau value G_p.

2) In a log-log diagram, if the G' curve in the lower frequency range shows a slope of 2:1 and the G'' curve has a slope of 1:1 *(Figure 16.4)*, this is called **Maxwellian behavior** or a **Maxwell fluid**, according to the physicist J.C. Maxwell (1831 to 1879). This behavior is a reliable indicator of **chemically or physically uncrosslinked polymers**. If this behavior is observed in partly crosslinked samples, then they do not have a consistent three-dimensional network.

For scientists working in polymer rheology, Maxwellian behavior is often a desired property because in this case the requirements for some evaluation methods are met that are interesting from the application technology point of view.

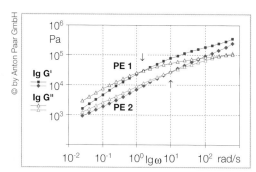

Figure 16.5: Frequency sweep at $\gamma = 10\ \%$ for comparing of two polyethylene melts (PE). The crossover point $G' = G''$ of PE1 appears at a lower frequency than that of PE2. This means that PE1 has a higher average molar mass than PE2.

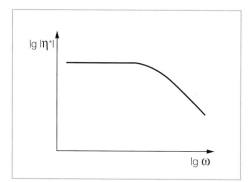

Figure 16.6: Frequency sweep of an uncrosslinked polymer, presentation of the function (of the total amount) of the complex viscosity $|\eta^*|$ showing the plateau value of the zero-shear viscosity in the lower frequency range.

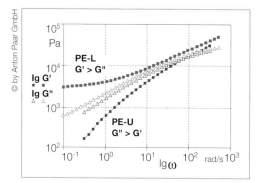

Figure 16.7: Frequency sweep at $\gamma = 1\ \%$ for the comparison of an uncrosslinked and a crosslinked polyethylene (PE). The uncrosslinked PE-U is a flowable melt with $G'' > G'$ in the lower frequency range. In contrast, the crosslinked PE-L with $G' > G''$ has a solid structure with $G' = 3000\ Pa$ at $\omega = 0.1\ rad/s$, which is almost at rest.

Example: Generation of WLF master curves (according to Williams / Landel / Ferry) using the method of time/temperature shift (TTS) or frequency/temperature shift (FTS), (see also [8]).

Measuring example:
Frequency sweep for comparing two polymer melts *(Figure 16.5)*

The properties of two polyethylenes PE1 and PE2 are compared at T = 180 °C and $\gamma = 10\ \%$. The measuring result shows that both PE melts have an uncrosslinked structure because both samples clearly show $G'' > G'$ in the lower frequency range. The crossover point ($G' = G''$) of PE1 occurs at $\omega = 1.8\ rad/s$ and that of PE2 at $\omega = 10\ rad/s$.

From this, it can be concluded that **the average molar mass M** of PE1 is higher than that of PE2.

Evaluation of the function of the complex viscosity $|\eta^*|$

Apart from the parameters storage modulus G' and loss modulus G'', some users also want to obtain viscosity values - despite the fact that this does not always make sense (as you will learn later). The value of the complex viscosity η^* (eta star) can be obtained in oscillatory tests, while in rotational tests the result is called the (shear) viscosity η (eta, no star). Calculation of the value of η^* (in Pas) is possible at every single measuring point via the values of the complex shear modulus G^* (in Pa) and angular frequency ω (in s^{-1}) at this point as follows:

$$|\eta^*| = G^* / \omega$$

Usually, the complex viscosity is written with two vertical bars (absolute value bars) in order to present it as the "total amount of eta star". This notation ensures that complex viscosity is always a non-negative value.

In the case of Maxwellian behavior, the curve of $|\eta^*|$ of **an uncrosslinked polymer** obtained by a frequency sweep **shows the plateau of the zero-shear viscosity** η_0 **in the lower frequency range** *(Figure 16.6)*. The value of η_0 is **proportional to the molar mass M**. This holds for polymer melts and polymer solutions that have the same polymer content. The plateau value is the same as that of the shear-rate or shear-stress-dependent viscosity function obtained in a rotational test (see *Chapter 6.2.2)*.

Measuring example:
Frequency sweep of an uncrosslinked polymer
Apart from showing the curves of G' and G'' from the frequency sweep on **silicone** (PDMS), *Figure 16.2* also presents the function of the complex viscosity $|\eta^*|$ with the plateau value of the zero-shear viscosity η_0 = 35 kPas. This high viscosity value indicates that, even though the silicone material is liquid, it will creep only very, very slowly due to its own weight when at rest. Here the shear rate corresponds to a value of approximately just 0.01 s^{-1}.
At ambient temperature and when applied to a vertical wall, for example, the silicone will flow at only 50 mm per hour. That really is slow motion in the low-shear range.

Furthermore, the criteria for **Maxwellian behavior** are also met in terms of the curve slopes in the lower-frequency range, with 2:1 for the G' function and 1:1 for the G'' function.

16.2 Crosslinked polymers
Measuring example:
Frequency sweeps for comparing crosslinked and uncrosslinked polymers
(Figure 16.7)
The aim was to compare two samples of a polyethylene with UV curable side chains; one sample before, and one sample after curing. Measurement parameters were T = +170 °C and γ = 1 %. Sample PE-U is a melt with an uncrosslinked structure, as can be seen from G'' > G' at lower frequencies, where it shows prevalently viscous behavior, and G' > G'' at higher frequencies. The crossover point G' = G'' is at ω = 70 rad/s.

In contrast, sample PE-L must have a crosslinked structure because, over the entire frequency range, the G' curve is above the G'' curve. Even though the two curves of G' and G'' of this sample approach each other very closely, there is no actual crossover point.
The G' value at a lower frequency can be used for comparison of the crosslinking density of different samples. The higher the G' value, the stiffer the material, and the higher the **degree of crosslinking**. At ω = 0.1 rad/s, PE-L shows a value of G' = 3000 Pa = 3 kPa.

Measuring example:

Frequency sweeps for comparing a liquid and a gelated resin *(Figure 16.8)*.

The two different resins should be drawn out of their respective containers with a suction pump. At **the start of the pumping process** it was evident that resin R1 could be pumped; the material continued to flow from the container wall to the tapping point all by itself. Resin R2, on the other hand, caused problems; it was not flowable and thus did not flow towards the pump. This could be verified in a frequency sweep; in particular, in the **low frequency range**, which simulates **behavior at rest**: R1 is liquid because $G'' > G'$, R2 is solid because $G' > G''$.

Furthermore, the diagram also shows the functions of the complex viscosity $|\eta^*|$. For R1, with its **uncrosslinked molecules**, the curve for $|\eta^*|$ in the range of decreasing frequency shows a tendency to reach the plateau of the **zero-shear viscosity** η_0. In this region, the viscosity would be relatively high, but not infinitely high. Even if R1 were able to flow here very, very slowly, at rest it would not be dimensionally stable in the long term. In contrast, for R2, with its **crosslinked molecules**, the $|\eta^*|$ curve in the range of decreasing frequency approaches infinity. This resin displays a solid consistency with a **certain dimensional stability** at rest.

Comment: This illustrates in which cases it really makes sense to evaluate the complex viscosity $|\eta^*|$ in practice. **Within the range where G' > G'', descriptions of $|\eta^*|$ are useless in practice** because, for very low frequencies, the $|\eta^*|$ curve approaches infinity. In practice, such a viscosity value means that the material is not flowable, but solid. It is therefore advisable, for gel structures, to only evaluate G' and G''. **For uncrosslinked polymers**, however, apart from G' and G'', the **plateau value of the zero-shear viscosity** η_0 is of practical significance.

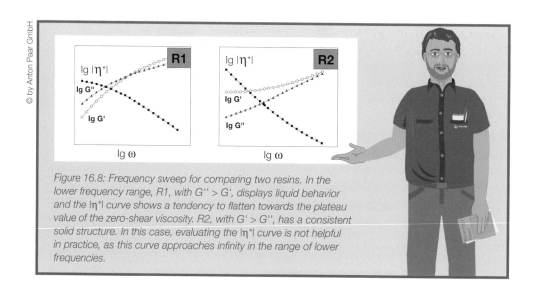

© by Anton Paar GmbH

Figure 16.8: Frequency sweep for comparing two resins. In the lower frequency range, R1, with $G'' > G'$, displays liquid behavior and the $|\eta^*|$ curve shows a tendency to flatten towards the plateau value of the zero-shear viscosity. R2, with $G' > G''$, has a consistent solid structure. In this case, evaluating the $|\eta^*|$ curve is not helpful in practice, as this curve approaches infinity in the range of lower frequencies.

16.3 Dispersions

Long-term storage behavior of dispersions is evaluated in the lower frequency range. If $G' > G''$, this indicates a solid structure, for example, caused by a stable network of forces. This fulfills the precondition for **physical dispersion stability**.

If, however, $G'' > G'$, this indicates that the material is liquid, and susceptible to **segregation**. In this case, effects such as **settling (sedimentation) or creaming (flotation)** can be expected.

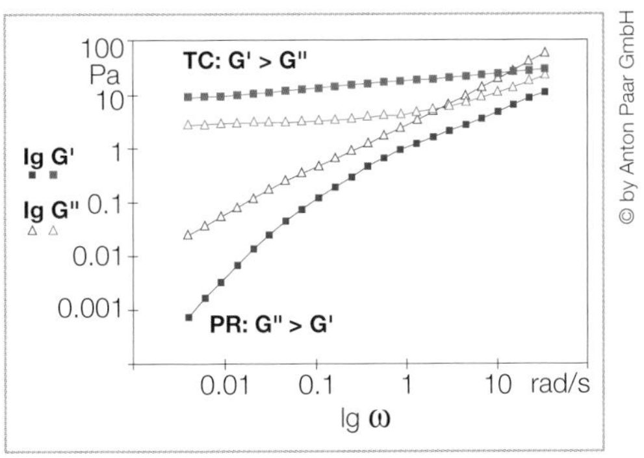

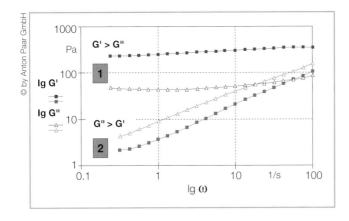

Figure 16.9: Frequency sweeps at $\gamma = 1$ % for comparing two spray coatings. Top coat TC, with $G' > G''$, has a solid structure and is therefore a stable dispersion. Primer PR, however, with $G'' > G'$, displays liquid behavior and thus has no stability.

© by Anton Paar GmbH

Measuring example:
Frequency sweep for testing the long-term storage stability of two spray coatings *(Figure 16.9)*

Two spray coatings were to be described and compared in terms of their **dispersion stability**. Measurement parameters were T = +23 °C and $\gamma = 1$ %.

In the frequency sweep, top coat TC showed a solid structure with $G' > G''$, which is due to an indeed weak, but nonetheless stable network of forces. The structural strength is about $G' = 10$ Pa. This fulfills the precondition for a certain dispersion stability. Primer PR consistently displayed a liquid character, with $G'' > G'$. No long-term storage stability can be expected for this product; rather, segregation.

Measuring example:
Frequency sweeps for testing the long-term storage stability of two coatings
(Figure 16.10)

A **water-based emulsion paint** was divided between two containers, along with a different **rheology additive** in each: A **clay silicate** as a gellant (1) in the first container

© by Anton Paar GmbH

Figure 16.10:
Frequency sweep at $\gamma = 1$ % for comparing the long-term storage stability of two water-based coatings with different rheology additives.
Sample 1 contains a gellant and is stable, as indicated by $G' > G''$.
Sample 2 contains an associative thickener and shows $G'' > G'$, which indicates instability.

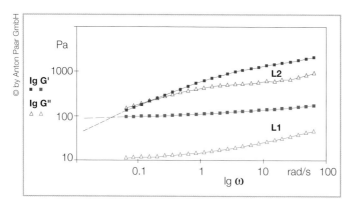

Figure 16.11:
Frequency sweep at
$\gamma = 0.3 \%$ *for comparing the*
dispersion stability of two
cosmetic lotions. With
$G' > G''$ *in the lower frequency*
range, L1 demonstrates a
certain amount of dispersion
stability. L2 shows $G'' > G'$ *in*
this range and therefore no
long-term storage stability can
be expected. For L1, the ratio
$G':G''$ *is rather high with 10:1;*
thus syneresis effects can be
anticipated.

and a polymeric **associative thickener** in the second (2). Measurement parameters for the frequency sweeps were $T = +23\,°C$ and $\gamma = 1\,\%$.

The long-term stability to sedimentation was assessed at low frequencies. The differences can clearly be seen. Dispersion 1, with $G' > G''$, meets the basic requirement for a stable structure. Its structural strength of $G' > 200$ Pa is comparable with that of a hand cream. On the other hand, dispersion 2, with $G'' > G'$, displays a predominantly viscous behavior and is therefore not a stable structure.

Measuring example:
Frequency sweeps to determine the dispersion stability of two cosmetic lotions
(Figure 16.11)

Two cosmetic solutions were described and compared in terms of their physical dispersion stability. A frequency sweep was carried out at $\gamma = 0.3\,\%$ and $T = +20\,°C$ with a step-wise decreasing angular frequency from $\omega = 62.8$ rad/s down to 0.0628 rad/s (which is equivalent to 10 Hz to 0.01 Hz). Lotion L1, with $G' > G''$, has a firm structure with strength of approximately $G' = 100$ Pa over the entire frequency range.

Lotion 2, however, with $G'' > G'$ in the range of low frequencies, displays a liquid character and therefore lacks long-term stability. This holds even though the G' value of L2 at the lowest frequency measured is greater than that of L1.

However, it is not the value of G' that is decisive here, but rather the viscoelastic character, i.e. whether $G' > G''$ or $G'' > G'$. Due to the solid and stable structure of L1, the G' value hardly changes across the entire frequency range, while the liquid behavior of L2 at rest only becomes evident below $\omega = 0.1$ rad/s.

Remark 1:
For evaluating long-term behavior, it is advisable to measure down to a frequency of $\omega = 0.01$ rad/s. In further tests, it was shown that the G' curves of L1 and L2 continue according to the dashed lines in the diagram, with a constant slope towards the left side of the diagram. At $\omega = 0.01$ rad/s, the lower structural strength at rest of L2, with $G' = 40$ Pa, becomes evident compared to L1 with $G' = 90$ Pa.

Remark 2:
L1 displays a solid structure, with $G' > G''$. However, if the ratio $G':G''$ becomes too large, **syneresis effects** that will show up as phase segregation should be taken into consideration. For L1, the ratio $G': G''$ is almost 10:1. The gel structure may be too stiff and inflexible.

Experience shows that most **emulsions and gels** with the same G' value; i.e., the same structural strength, are stable against low agitation, and are flexible to a certain degree, if $G': G''$ is within the range of 3:1 to 5:1. Many users express this with the inverse value, the loss factor $\tan\delta = G''/G'$. Correspondingly, gel-like structures are often resistant against syneresis if $\tan\delta$ shows a value between 0.2 and 0.3.

Remark 3:
Rheology tests can be used to assess **physical dispersion stability** but not biological long-term stability, for example against microbial activities.

17. Time-dependent behavior (oscillation)

For evaluating time-dependent viscoelastic behavior, oscillatory tests are performed with shearing under constant dynamic-mechanical conditions. This means: Both amplitude and frequency are kept constant for each individual test interval.

17.1 Time-dependent structural regeneration after shearing, and thixotropic behavior

Possible applications:

After application, coatings will rebuild structural strength within a certain period of time; for example, spray coatings, printing inks or food, such as ketchup *(Figures 17.1 to 17.3).*

The following requirements hold for structural regeneration. It should be:
a) not too fast, to allow for good **levelling**, but also
b) not too slow in order to prevent **sagging**, and to ensure a sufficient **wet-layer thickness**.

© by Anton Paar GmbH

Figure 17.1: Spray coatings should show good levelling behavior after application but their tendency to sagging should be limited.

Figure 17.2: Ketchup on french fries is an illustrative example for the behavior of coatings after application. Sample 1 shows very fast structural recovery, resulting in high dimensional stability. Sample 2, in contrast, rebuilds its structure only very slowly; it flows and levels for longer, leaving a small wet-layer thickness.

Figure 17.3:
Printing inks after the printing process under a magnifying glass:
In halftone printing, reproduction with sharp edges and precise dot definition is desired (left and right). An inadequate print quality is shown in the picture in the middle [12].

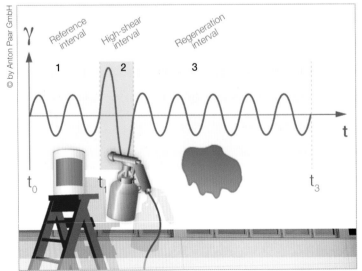

© by Anton Paar GmbH

Figure 17.4:
Preset profile for an oscillatory step test with three intervals used to simulate the behavior of a spray coating:
(1) constant low strain, as in the state at rest,
(2) constant high strain, as applied in a coating process,
(3) structural regeneration at rest after application, showing the same low strain as in the first interval.
For all three test intervals, the measuring system oscillates at the same frequency.

a) Step test with preset oscillation for all three test intervals

Step tests are used for evaluating the breakdown of the inner structure of a sample under high shear, and its subsequent recovery. It can be performed as an oscillatory test with the following three test intervals. Usually a time-dependent strain profile is preset *(Figure 17.4)*.

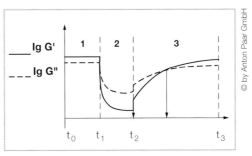

© by Anton Paar GmbH

Figure 17.5: Possible result of an oscillatory step test with three intervals, showing the time-dependent functions of G' and G'': (1) solid state, at rest with G' > G''; (2) liquid behavior, with G'' > G' during structural breakdown induced by high shear and (3) at rest during structural regeneration, showing crossover point G' = G'' and then finally, G' > G'' in a solid state again.

(1) Very low shear to **simulate behavior at rest** at low strain within the LVE region,
(2) Strong shear to **simulate structural breakdown of the sample during application** at high strain far beyond the LVE region,
(3) Very low shear to **simulate structural regeneration at rest** using the same low strain value as in the first test interval.
Usually, the same (angular) frequency is preset for all three test intervals.

The result is commonly presented as time-dependent functions of G' and G''
(Figure 17.5):
(1) Behavior nearly at rest,
(2) Behavior during structural breakdown when shearing is stronger,
(3) Behavior during structural recovery nearly at rest.
The diagram shows a solid structure in the first test interval (with G' > G''), a liquid structure in the second interval (with G'' > G') and finally a solid structure again after exceeding the crossover point G' = G''.

Definition of **thixotropic behavior**, in this case relating to the storage modulus G' (according to DIN/TR 91143-2):
Thixotropic behavior is characterized by a decrease in the values of rheological parameters such as storage modulus G' against a constant, time-independent limiting value due to constant mechanical load, and **the complete time-dependent recovery of the initial state upon reduction of the load**.

Correspondingly, the following counts for **rheopectic behavior** which, however, is rarely found in practical applications: Rheopectic behavior is characterized by an **increase** in the values of rheological parameters such as G' against a constant, time-independent limiting value due to constant mechanical load, and the complete time-dependent recovery of the initial state upon reduction of the load.

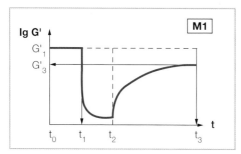

Figure 17.6: Method M1 to evaluate structural regeneration: Regeneration in the third test interval is determined at a previously defined point in time, and is quoted as a percentage of the G' value at rest at the end of the first interval.
The diagram shows, for example 80 % regeneration at time-point t_3.

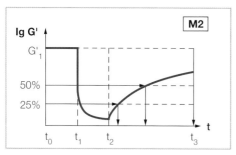

Figure 17.7: Method M2 to analyze structural regeneration: Determination of the points at which there has been 25 % or 50 % regeneration, for example, in the third test interval, related to the G' value at rest at the end of the first interval.

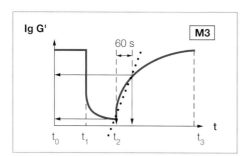

Figure 17.8: Method M3 to investigate structural regeneration: Determination of the slope of the time-dependent G' function curve during regeneration; for example, within the first 60 s of the third interval.

Methods for evaluating time-dependent structural regeneration
(according to DIN/TR 91143-2)
In order to evaluate structural regeneration in the third test interval based on G' values, the following methods, M1 to M4, can be applied: The G' value at rest at the end of the first test interval is used as a reference value for M1 and M2. M4 is the preferred method for evaluating thixotropic behavior.

(M1) Determination of structural regeneration as a percentage of that reached at a previously defined time-point or, alternatively, at the end of the third test interval *(Figure 17.6)*.

Example of M1:
After 60 s in the third test interval, regeneration reached 80 % of the reference value.

(M2) Determination of the time-points for a defined regeneration as a percentage *(Figure 17.7)*

Example of M2:
A 25% regeneration was achieved after 30 s, and a 50% regeneration after 90 s.

(M3) Slope of the time-dependent G' function during regeneration within a previously defined time interval *(Figure 17.8)*

Example of M3:
In the third test interval, the G' value increases in the period $\Delta t = 60$ s from $G' = 20$ Pa to 50 Pa; the difference is $\Delta G' = 30$ Pa. From the diagram, this results in a value for the slope of $(\Delta G' / \Delta t) = (30 \text{ Pa}/60 \text{ s}) = 0.5$ Pa/s.

(M4) Time-point at the crossover point of G' and G'' in the third test interval *(Figure 17.5)*.

Example of M4:
In the third test interval, the crossover point G' = G'' is reached after 30 s.

Figures 17.9 and *17.10* illustrate the practical effects of time-dependent structural regeneration after application, for three **spray coatings**. The blue coating has too slow a regeneration and will sag too much and over too long a period of time (left). The green coating, on the other hand, has too quick a regeneration, resulting in insufficient levelling and, finally, in an uneven surface (middle). Finally, the red coating has a **balanced regeneration time that is neither too long nor too short**, displaying the desired behavior with sufficient levelling and a negligible tendency to sagging (right).

Measuring example:
Undesired dripping of adhesive from the cartridge *(Figure 17.11)*
Individual glue dots were applied with an SMD (surface mounted device) adhesive on a circuit board to fasten electronic devices on the board for the subsequent mounting and soldering process. The problem in practice was that the adhesive kept dripping from the applicator's nozzle after application of the glue dot. The application was simulated with the following step test, but not before the limit of the LVE region was determined in an amplitude sweep.

© by Anton Paar GmbH

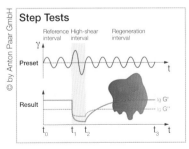
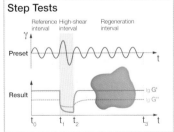
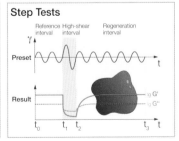

Figure 17.9: The following situation was demonstrated: First all three spray coatings are at rest, next they are subjected to high shearing during spray application, and finally they are left alone to come to rest again.

© by Anton Paar GmbH

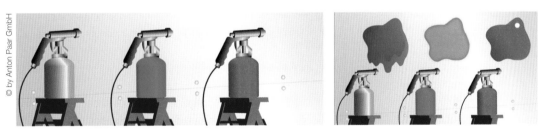

Figure 17.10: Evaluation of the structural regeneration of the three spray coatings after application:
The blue coating has too slow a regeneration and therefore is prone to sagging (left).
The green coating rebuilds too fast, which finally results in an uneven surface (middle).
Only the red coating has a balanced regeneration time and delivers the desired "glossy" result.

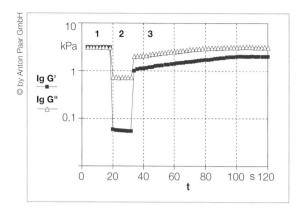

Figure 17.11: Result of an oscillatory step test with three intervals showing the time-dependent functions of G' and G'' used for evaluating the structural regeneration of an SMD adhesive: (1) behavior at rest with G' = G'', (2) flowable when sheared, with G'' > G', and (3) insufficient structural regeneration after release. The result: continued dripping.

Preset for the first and third test intervals was $\gamma_1 = \gamma_3 = 0.2$ % in order to simulate the behavior at rest before and after high shearing. For the second test interval, the strain was set to $\gamma_2 = 100$ % in order to simulate the flow behavior when pressing the glue out of the cartridge. Measurement parameters for all three intervals were T = +23 °C and $\omega = 10$ rad/s.

Evaluation: At rest G'' = G', which means that the viscous and the elastic portions of the viscoelastic sample are the same size. You would experience this if you were standing exactly in the **middle of Rheology Road**. However, this does not mean that the adhesive is liquid at rest. When sheared, it flows as desired, because then clearly G'' > G'. In fact, G'' is now ten times higher than G'. This indicates good flowability. When returning to a state of rest, the structure of the adhesive does not recover completely, even after ≥ 60 s. The adhesive shows G'' > G', which means that it is still liquid, even though it has a much higher viscosity than in the second test interval. This explains the continued dripping.

The problem could quickly be solved with a rheology additive. This additive is now used in the production process to impart a slightly higher G' than G'' in the first interval. During the second interval, the material remains liquid with G'' > G', while the requirement for G' > G'' in the third test interval is met within just a few seconds.

b) Step test as an ORO test

Often a process needs to be simulated with a focus on practical aspects. In such a case, it makes sense that the step test is modified accordingly because, even with a high strain amplitude in the second test interval, shear rates above 100 s⁻¹ cannot really be achieved. Therefore, a mixed test is recommended; for example, with the following three test intervals:

Oscillation / Rotation / Oscillation, also known as ORO test *(Figure 17.12)*:

(1) Oscillation at very low shear to **simulate behavior at rest**, performed at a low strain value from the LVE region.

(2) Rotational test at strong shear to **simulate structural breakdown of the sample during application**, performed at a high shear rate.

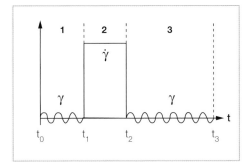

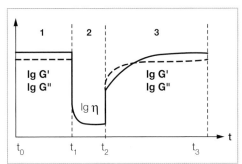

Figure 17.12: Preset profile for a step test with three intervals to evaluate breakdown and recovery of the sample's structure, here as an ORO test: (1) Oscillation at a constant low strain amplitude, (2) Rotation at a constant high shear rate, (3) Oscillation at the same low strain amplitude as in the first interval.

Figure 17.13: Possible result of an oscillatory step test with three intervals, showing the time-dependent functions of G' and G'', as well as of shear viscosity η: (1) solid state at rest with G' > G'' (oscillation), (2) structural breakdown induced by high shearing with a decrease in viscosity (rotation), (3) at rest again during structural regeneration showing the crossover point G' = G'' and finally, in a solid state again, with G' > G'' (oscillation). This example shows complete regeneration of the structure.

(3) Oscillation at very low shear to **simulate structural regeneration at rest**, performed using the same low strain value from the LVE region as in the first test interval.
For both test intervals using oscillation, the same (angular) frequency is preset.

The results of the measurement are presented as time-dependent functions of the storage modulus G', loss modulus G'' and shear viscosity η *(Figure 17.13)*:
(1) Behavior nearly at rest,
(2) Behavior during structural breakdown under high shear conditions,
(3) Behavior during structural recovery nearly at rest.
The diagram shows a solid structure in the first test interval (with G' > G''), a liquid structure in the second interval, and finally a solid structure again after exceeding the crossover point G' = G''.

Measuring example: Structural regeneration of a dispersion after a filling process
(Figure 17.14)
After bottling, a dispersion should rebuild its structure not too slowly, in order to prevent too much segregation. Examples include **pharmaceutical** or **medicinal products** with active agents such as **cough syrup**. The step test performed was an ORO test at T = +23 °C. For the first and third test intervals, oscillation was preset at a strain amplitude of $\gamma_1 = \gamma_3 = 1\ \%$ and an angular frequency of $\omega = 10$ rad/s. These parameters should simulate the behavior at rest before and after the high shear process of bottling. In the second test interval, the bottling process itself was simulated with $\dot{\gamma} = 100\ s^{-1}$.

Evaluation:

The initial, slightly gel-like structure (with $G' > G''$ and the very low structural strength of $G' = 0.25$ Pa) is destroyed in the second test interval.

The structure recovers slowly in the third interval and reaches crossover point $G' = G''$ after $t = 115$ s.

Finally, the dispersion recovers to its initial state, in terms of both G' and G''. Therefore, it is correct to call this behavior thixotropic.

Measuring example:

Sag control of automotive coatings by an ORO test *(Figures 17.15 to 17.17)*
Automotive spray coatings AC1 to AC3 contain different amounts of rheology

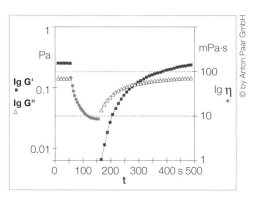

Figure 17.14: Result of an ORO step test with three intervals on a thixotropic dispersion.
Solid state with $G' > G''$ in the first interval, structural breakdown with viscosity reduction in the second interval, and structural regeneration in the third interval, liquid at first with $G'' > G'$, the solid state with $G' > G''$ is reached after about two minutes.

additives. The tendency to sagging after application for all three coatings was tested in a three-interval step test. The measuring temperature was $T = +23$ °C. According to the ORO test, the first and third intervals were performed as oscillatory tests, with $\gamma = 0.2$ % and $\omega = 10$ rad/s, while the second interval was carried out at $\dot{\gamma} = 15{,}000$ s^{-1}.

The evaluation shows huge differences in the third interval regarding the structural recovery of the coatings. The result for AC1 without rheology additive is clearly $G'' > G'$, even after $t = 300$ s, thus indicating strong sagging. AC2, which contains an additive, displays fast recovery but still shows $G'' > G'$ after 300 s. This is still not satisfactory. For AC3, finally, with a balanced mixture of two rheology additives the crossover point $G' = G''$ appears within the desired period of time. After that time, the structure of this coating shows sufficient solidity to prevent sagging. The ORO step test is thus a suitable test method to check and control sagging behavior of coatings by use of rheology additives.

Figure 17.15:
Automotive coating process using an electrostatic high-rotational robotic spray system. ORO tests can be used for sag control of spray coatings.

© by Anton Paar GmbH

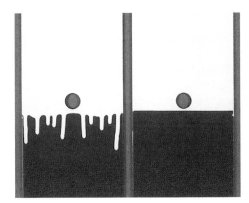

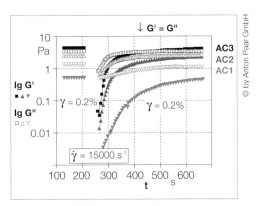

© by Anton Paar GmbH

Figure 17.16: Sag-control test of a pigmented high-solid top coating after spray application using upright-positioned paint-sagging sheets, on the right with a rheology additive, on the left without. The latter (left) shows sagging [5].

Figure 17.17: ORO step test with three intervals to compare three automotive spray coatings, evaluation of time-dependent structural regeneration in the third test interval:
After t = 300 s, AC1 and AC2 still show G'' > G'.
This means they are still liquid and tend to sag.
For AC3, G' = G'' is reached after 180 s.
After that period of time, the coating is solid and does not sag.

Remark:
Comparison of step tests via rotation or oscillation, in particular with respect to the test interval showing structural regeneration.
a) There is only one measuring parameter for tests with preset rotation in all three intervals, and that is the (shear) viscosity η. In such tests, only the viscous behavior can be directly evaluated; the elastic portion of the behavior cannot be determined.
b) In contrast, step tests carried out as oscillatory tests for all three intervals, or as a mixed ORO test, deliver two measuring parameters for structural regeneration, namely G' and G''.
This allows the viscous behavior as well as the elastic behavior – thus **the entire viscoelastic behavior** – to be evaluated. Only if both portions are balanced in terms of time dependence can the desired behavior be achieved.

17.2 Time-dependent behavior with gel formation or curing

This oscillatory test is performed under **constant dynamic-mechanical conditions.** Accordingly, both parameters – shear-strain (or shear-stress) amplitude and (angular) frequency – are kept constant in this test. In most cases, controlled-strain tests (or CSD, resp.) are preferred. One disadvantage of controlled-shear-stress tests is that, with increasing values of G' and G'', the resulting deflection angle will decrease continuously. This would result in the degree of deformation no longer being constant. However, the latter is a decisive parameter for comparing the effects that shearing has on the behavior of a sample.
Furthermore, the measuring temperature is kept constant thus providing for isothermal conditions. It is recommended that **disposable measuring systems are used, consisting of a disposable plate and a disposable dish** for single use (see *Figure 3.5).*

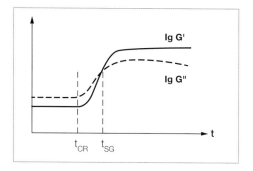

Figure 17.18: Time-dependent functions of G' and G'' of a gel-forming or curing sample, here shown on a semi-logarithmic scale: Both curves increase significantly after reaching time-point t_{CR} since here the gel-formation or curing reaction begins. The time-point t_{SG} of the sol/gel transition has been reached at the crossover point G' = G''.

The result is usually evaluated as time-dependent functions of G' and G'' *(Figure 17.18)*. There are two time-points that are of special interest: The time-point t_{CR} where the curve of the G' function starts to rise at **the beginning of a gel-formation or chemical-curing process**, as well as the time-point t_{SG} at the **crossover point G' = G'' as the sol/gel transition point**, often also just called the **gel point**. In addition, the **final values of G' and G''** are evaluated in many cases.

Measuring example:
Curing times of a powder coating at different temperatures *(Figure 17.19)*
The aim of the test is to compare the curing behavior of an epoxy powder coating at three different temperatures under **isothermal conditions**. For the test, **disposable PP measuring systems** were used at a constant strain of $\gamma = 0.1$ % and a constant angular frequency of $\omega = 10$ rad/s. The constant measuring temperatures were T = 120 °C, 140 °C and 160 °C.
The time-point t_{SG} of the sol/gel transition at the crossover point G' = G'' was evaluated for each test. In all three cases, G'' > G' in the beginning, which means that the powder coating was already in a molten state at each of the three temperatures. It can be seen that - as expected - the speed of the **curing reaction** increases with temperature.
At T = 120 °C, the gel point t_{SG} will occur after 1370 s, at T = 140 °C after $t_{SG} = 360$ s, and at T = 160 °C after only $t_{SG} = 140$ s.

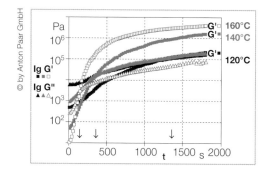

Figure 17.19: Time-dependent behavior of a powder coating: isothermal tests performed at three constant measuring temperatures; T = 120 °C, 140 °C and 160 °C. The three time-points indicated on the x-axis show the sol/gel transitions, which occur at the crossover points G' = G''. The higher the temperature, the faster the curing reaction.

Measuring example:
Comparison of curing times for two powder coatings using a two-stage temperature profile *(Figure 17.20)*

The aim of the test is to investigate the curing behavior of two epoxy powder coatings, PC1 and PC2, using a two-stage temperature profile that has been adapted to the processing conditions. For the test, a **disposable PP measuring system** was used, with preset parameters $\gamma = 0.1$ % and $\omega = 10$ rad/s. The time-dependent temperature profile T(t) consisted of two test intervals:

1) Heating in the form of a linear ramp from T = 150 to 180 °C until reaching time-point t = 280 s.

2) Holding phase at a constant temperature of T = 180 °C for 560 s.

This temperature profile should simulate the following situation: First, the material is coated at a lower temperature before it is placed in the hot oven, where it is heated and continues to melt before the curing process starts. Finally, the coating reaches the preset constant oven temperature and cures completely. Evaluation of the curves of G' and G'' provides the following information in terms of the softening and curing process:

a) For PC1, **the beginning of the curing reaction**, as indicated by the minimum in G', is seen at t = 200 s, and as soon as t = 150 s for PC2.

b) PC 1 reached the **sol/gel transition** or gel point t_{SG} , as indicated by the crossover point G' = G'', after t = 490 s, while PC2 had already reached this point by t = 210 s, which is still during the heating phase.

c) **At the end of the curing process**, PC1 has a **final stiffness** comparable with that of a soft rubber eraser, as seen in its final G' value of more than 500,000 Pa = 0.5 MPa, whereas PC2, with G' = 140,000 Pa = 0.14 MPa, has only one third of that value, thus creating a **soft touch effect**.

Measuring example:
UV curing of a resin *(Figure 17.21)*

The aim of the test was to investigate the time-dependent curing process of a UV curing reaction resin at T = +23 °C. The presets were $\gamma = 0.1$ % and $\omega = 10$ rad/s. The

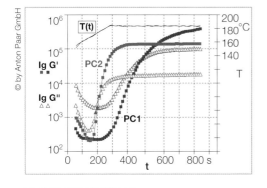

Figure 17.20: Comparison of two powder coatings heated with a defined temperature profile. The curing reaction starts where G' is at a minimum and the sol/gel transition occurs at G' = G''. PC1 cures more slowly and reaches a higher final G' value, and therefore a higher degree of final stiffness.

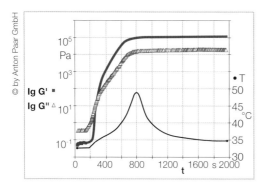

Figure 17.21: Curing process of a UV-curing-reaction resin with the time-dependent functions of G' and G''. The gel point at G' = G'' is reached after 280 s. The temperature curve (black line) illustrates the exothermic reaction, with an increasing reaction rate, producing a rising temperature up to a maximum at t = 800 s, the reaction rate then decreasing again.

measuring system used was a **plate/plate geometry, with the bottom plate made of a UV-light-transmitting quartz glass** *(Figure 17.22)*. A UV light source mounted below the glass plate radiates the light into the sample at constant intensity.

Initially, G'' > G', indicating liquid behavior. After 140 s, the curing process starts, seen in the steeply rising curves. **The crossover point G' = G''** appears after 280 s. Afterwards, G' dominates, indicating solid behavior. Finally, the following plateau values were reached after approximately 800 s:
G' = 100,000 Pa = 100 kPa and G'' = 20 kPa.
The cured resin or elastomer with G' = 100 kPa = 0.1 MPa is approximately ten times less stiff than a rubber eraser. This is known as **soft touch**, which can be experienced inside a car on the dashboard, or the armrest on a sofa, for example.

With a separate sensor placed directly inside the measuring gap, the temperature curve of the curing resin could be measured as well. Apart from the rheological and mechanical effects described by the curves of G' and G'', the user also wanted to visualize the thermal effects of the **exothermic crosslinking reaction**, which releases heat. The heating process starts at the same time as the increase in the values of G' and G''. After reaching the **temperature maximum** at 800 s, the chemical reaction rate decreases, with the values of G' and G'' flattening simultaneously. The density of crosslinks is no longer increasing; the sample has achieved its final stiffness.

The results for the rheological or physical-mechanical behavior and for the thermal or chemical behavior coincide well in terms of time.

Figure 17.22: Plate/plate system with a transparent bottom plate made of quartz glass for testing light-curing materials, such as UV-curing resins.

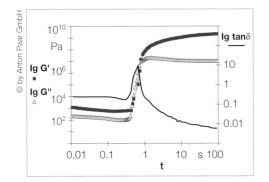
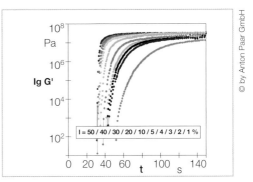

Figure 17.23: Curing process of a UV-curing-reaction resin: presentation of the time-dependent functions of G' and G''. The gel point at G' = G'' is reached after just under 1 s. For evaluation of reaction time, the curve maximum of loss factor tanδ was used here (shown as the black line). As an exception, a logarithmic scale was used for time t.

*Figure 17.24: Curing process of a UV-curing printing ink at various relative UV-light intensities I between 1 and 50 %.
At higher light intensity, the curing reaction rate increases more rapidly, as does the G' value.*

Measuring example:
Very fast UV curing of a resin *(Figure 17.23)*

For evaluating the curing behavior of a UV-curing-reaction resin, a **plate/plate geometry with a diameter of just 8 mm** was used. The bottom plate was made of a light-transmitting quartz glass (as was shown in *Figure 17.22*). The following constant measuring parameters were preset:

$\gamma = 0.02$ %, $\omega = 62.8$ rad/s, measuring temperature T = +20 °C.

Considering the **very fast chemical reaction**, and to achieve a faster measuring point sequence, an angular frequency of $\omega = 62.8$ rad/s (corresponding to a frequency of f = 10 Hz) was chosen instead of the commonly used angular frequency of $\omega = 10$ rad/s. To visualize the rapid curing process, time (t) on the x-axis is plotted on a logarithmic scale. The sample is already pasty prior to curing, reflected in G' > G'', with G' = 800 to 1000 Pa and G'' = 100 to 200 Pa. The curing process starts very quickly, as early as t = 0.3 s.

After just 1 s, the **crossover point G' = G''** is reached. For evaluation of the reaction time, the **curve maximum of the loss factor tanδ** (= G''/ G') was used.

After 10 s, G' is greater than 1 GPa, and is up to 2 GPa by 100 s.

The cured resin now shows the behavior of a stiff and rigid solid matter.

Measuring example:
UV curing of a printing ink *(Figure 17.24)*

The aim of the test was to analyze the time-dependent curing process of a UV curing printing ink at T = +23 °C. Presets were $\gamma = 0.1$ % and $\omega = 10$ rad/s. The measuring system used was a plate/plate geometry with the bottom plate made of quartz glass. Ten tests were performed **at different light intensities** between 1 % and 50 %. The result was as expected: The higher the UV-light intensity, the faster the curing process, here shown by the time-dependent G' values.

18. Temperature-dependent behavior (oscillation)

For evaluating temperature-dependent viscoelastic behavior, shearing in oscillatory tests is performed under constant dynamic-mechanical conditions. This means that both amplitude and frequency are kept constant. It is only the temperature that changes according to a preset profile. As a result, the temperature-dependent functions of G' and G'' are usually analyzed.

In order to minimize the **temperature gradient within the measuring chamber** which contains the sample, it is advisable to use **special temperature-control devices** which are equipped with **Peltier elements**. There are two types of systems; one featuring a "**passive hood**" without temperature control, and another with an "**active hood**" where the temperature can be controlled (see *Chapter 10* and *Figure 10.1*).

18.1 Temperature-dependent behavior without chemical modification
Typical tests in this field are used for investigating **softening** or **melting** behavior of samples when **heated**; or **solidification, crystallization** or **cold gelation** when **cooled**. Such tests are performed at constant shear conditions. Hence, the parameters shear-strain (or shear-stress) amplitude as well as (angular) frequency are kept constant in this test. A defined temperature profile is preset, for example with a temperature gradient of 1 °C per minute.

Measuring example:
Melting process of a polymer blend *(Figure 18.1)*
The aim of this test was to determine the melting temperature of an **ABS polymer**.

ABS is a blend of three immiscible polymers; acrylonitrile, butadiene and styrene. Preset parameters for the temperature range from +180 °C to +280 °C were $\gamma = 1$ % and $\omega = 10$ rad/s as well as a **heating rate** of $\Delta T/\Delta t = 1$ °C/min. At the start, the sample is solid, with G' > G''. At the crossover point G' = G'', the **melting temperature** of $T_m = 215$ °C has been reached.

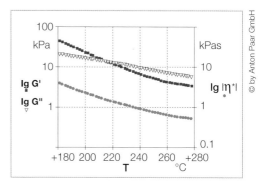

Figure 18.1: Heating of a polymer blend (ABS), showing softening and melting. At the crossover point G' = G'', the melting temperature of 215 °C has been reached. The curve of the complex viscosity |η*| is also presented. However, this curve is not an indicator for the melting temperature.

a) Thermal behavior of polymers

Temperature sweeps are often performed to characterize polymer structures and, in particular, to describe the internal superstructure and configuration of the macromolecules. The temperature-dependent functions of storage modulus G' and loss modulus G'' (and sometimes the loss factor $\tan\delta = G''/ G'$ as a ratio of both moduli) are usually presented. The two most important parameters for the evaluation are:

1) Glass-transition temperature T_g, which is found approximately in the middle of the **glass-transition range**. When heating a cold and rigid polymer, the glass-transition range starts at the first signs of softening and ends when the molten state has been completely reached. The value of T_g depends significantly on the heating or cooling rate. Several evaluation methods are available that are described in various standards. For many users, the following is the method of choice and this is why it is recommended here: **The temperature at G'' maximum is taken as T_g** (see the standards ASTM D4065, D4092, E1640). Alternatively, the temperature at the maximum of the $\tan\delta$ curve can be taken as T_g (as also stated in ASTM E1640). The latter method usually results in a higher T_g than that determined from the G'' maximum. Therefore, the analysis method used should always be stated in the test protocol.

2) The melting temperature T_m, which is the temperature at the crossover point G' = G''.

Materials scientists usually distinguish three polymer groups based on the configuration of the macromolecules in the cold state; 1) amorphous polymers, 2) partially crystalline polymers and 3) crosslinked polymers:

1) Amorphous polymers are chemically uncrosslinked, and in the molten state the individual molecules can move freely. In the cold state, the so-called **glassy state**, G' > G''. Here, the molecules show a disordered superstructure. T_g is determined at G'' maximum; usually T_m is not stated because T_g and T_m are often very close (Figure 18.2).

Measuring example:
Thermal behavior of a polymer-
modified bitumen *(Figure 18.3)*
The aim of the test was to determine the temperature-dependent behavior of a polymer-modified **bitumen** (PMB) during **heating and melting** in the temperature range from T = -20 °C to +100 °C. PMB is used as a **binder for asphalt in road constructions**.

Amplitude sweeps were performed at temperatures of -20 °C, +35 °C and +100 °C, in order to first determine the limit of the LVE region. For the temperature sweep, the strain was preset in two steps; T = -20 to +35 °C with $\gamma = 0.1$ %, and T = +35 to 100 °C with $\gamma = 1$ %. This was necessary for obtaining good results, because the G' values cover such a large range (seven decades). For both test intervals, $\omega = 10$ rad/s was preset.
Evaluation of the functions of G' and G''
shows that the transition between the two temperature intervals, i.e. at T = +35 °C, is acceptably smooth. Despite the fact that the polymer in the PMB is just 2 wt% of the total mass of the sample, the temperature curves reflect almost exclusively the viscoelastic behavior of the polymer component; i.e., a superstructure of filamentary, relatively long and entangled molecules.

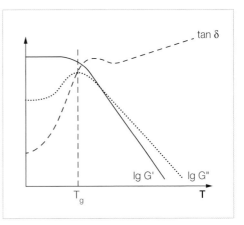

Figure 18.2: Temperature-dependent functions of G', G'' and tanδ for an amorphous polymer, showing the glass-transition temperature T_g at G'' maximum.

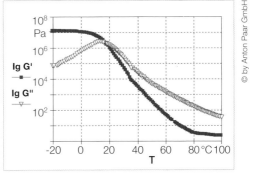

Figure 18.3: Temperature-dependent functions of G' and G'' for a polymer-modified bitumen (PMB). The glass-transition temperature $T_g = +17$ °C was read at G'' maximum.
The binder used displays typical behavior of an amorphous polymer.

At T = -20 °C, the sample is in the so-called **glassy state**, which means it is very stiff and rigid. G' in this state is about 100 x higher than G''. This means that almost ideal-elastic behavior prevails here, with a viscous portion of just 1 %. The **glass-transition temperature**, $T_g = +17$ °C, was taken as **G'' maximum**. The binder used shows the typical **behavior of an amorphous polymer**, in that G' and G'' drop steadily after T_g has been exceeded.

2) Partially crystalline polymers are chemically uncrosslinked, and in a molten state the individual molecules can move freely. In the cold state, G' > G''. There are some regions where the molecules show an ordered, crystalline super-structure. These regions are firmer, and are surrounded by amorphous regions without ordered superstructure. T_g is evaluated at G'' maximum, and T_m at the crossover point G' = G'' *(Figure 18.4)*. One characteristic feature of partially crystalline materials is the rather distinct plateau of the curves of G' and G'' between T_g and T_m. This is called the **rubber-elastic plateau**. In this region, the amorphous portion is already molten, while most parts of the crystalline portion are not yet molten. In this state, the polymer is neither unambiguously liquid nor unambiguously solid; in essence, it is in an undefined state. In the plateau region, G' and G'' have almost the same value. The behavior is essentially swaying back and forth across the middle of Rheology Road.

Figure 18.4: Temperature-dependent functions of G', G'' and tanδ for a partially crystalline polymer with glass-transition temperature T_g at G'' maximum and melting temperature T_m at crossover point G' = G'', showing the distinct plateaus of the G' and G'' curves between T_g and T_m

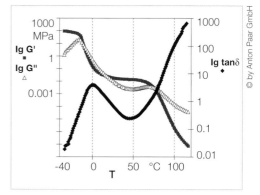

Measuring example: Thermal behavior of a hot-melt adhesive *(Figure 18.5)*
The temperature-dependent behavior of a hot-melt adhesive **during heating and melting** in the range of T = -35 to +115 °C was analyzed. Measurement parameters were γ = 1 % und ω = 10 rad/s.

Figure 18.5: Temperature-dependent functions of G', G'' and tanδ for a partially crystalline hot-melt adhesive with a distinct rubber-elastic plateau of the G' curve between T_g = -18 °C at G'' maximum and T_m = +75 °C at the crossover point G' = G''.

Evaluation of the functions of G' and G'' shows the typical **behavior of an uncrosslinked, partially crystalline polymer** with a pronounced **rubber-elastic plateau** between +10 °C and +60 °C. At T = -35 °C, the sample is very stiff and rigid. The ratio of G' to G'' is 100:1, which means that the elastic behavior strongly predominates.

The **glass-transition temperature** is T_g = -18 °C, as evaluated from G'' maximum. **By the way:** If you evaluated the tanδ maximum, T_g would be 0° C. The difference of 18 °C between the two evaluation methods is rather large in this case. The melting temperature is T_m = 75 °C at the crossover point G' = G'' or at tanδ = G'' / G' = 1.

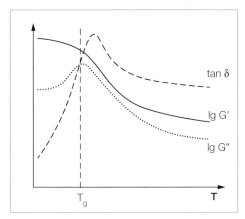

Figure 18.6: Temperature-dependent functions of G', G'' and tanδ of a cross-linked polymer with glass-transition temperature T_g at the maximum of G''. Even in the heated state, the material does not show the character of a flowable melt because G' > G''.

3) Crosslinked polymers are characterized by stable chemical bonds between the polymer molecules. Thus the individual molecules in the molten state are not able to move freely, but rather, are firmly embedded in a three-dimensional network formed by strong bonds. Examples include **crosslinked elastomers, vulcanized rubber and cured thermosets**. In the cold state, G' > G''. T_g occurs at G'' maximum. When heated, the material softens to a certain extent, but it does not melt. In this situation, the chemical bonds remain stable, as long as the temperature is not too high. Therefore, here again G' > G'' *(Figure 18.6).*

Many crosslinked elastomers have **bridges between the polymer chains** consisting of between 200 and 400 C atoms; for wide-meshed polymers it can even be up to 1,000 C atoms (C stands for carbon). In contrast, the bridges in close-meshed cured thermosets are often just 20 C atoms long.

Measuring example:
Thermal behavior of a crosslinked elastomer *(Figure 18.7)*
The temperature-dependent behavior of a crosslinked elastomer (rubber) during heating in the range of T = -80 to +160 °C was tested. Preset were the constant dynamic shear conditions $\gamma = 0$, 25 % and $\omega = 10$ rad/s.

The curves of the functions of G' and G'' show the typical behavior of a **chemically crosslinked elastomer** with G' > G'', even at high temperatures. Thus, the sample is still in a solid state. The **glass-transition temperature** is $T_g = -22$ °C, as evaluated

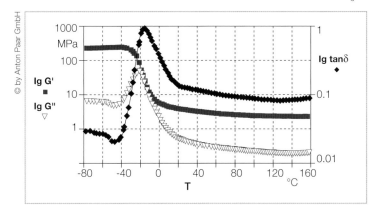

Figure 18.7: Temperature-dependent functions of G', G'' and tanδ of a crosslinked elastomer with $T_g = -22$ °C at G'' maximum. Even at high temperatures of up to 160 °C, the sample remains in a solid state because G' > G''.

at G'' maximum. For comparison: If evaluated at tanδ maximum, it would be T_g = -16° C. The following values were used for evaluating the stiffness of the rubber sample. Frozen at T = -80 °C in the so-called glassy state, G' = 220 MPa. At ambient temperature (T = +20 °C), G' = 4.4 MPa. The hot elastomer at T = 160 °C is still solid with G' = 2.2 MPa. However, it is now one hundred times softer than in the cold state.

b) Thermal behavior of crystallizing solutions and dispersions

When crystallizing solutions and dispersions are heated and molten, or cooled down and solidified in the region of their **crystallization temperature** T_k, the curves of G' and G'', and that of tanδ show a sharp decrease or increase, respectively, within a very narrow temperature range (Figure 18.8).

Measuring example:
Thermal behavior of a crystallizing emulsion (Figure 18.9)

The aim of the test was to determine the **cooling** behavior of an emulsion that was to be launched as a **cosmetic lotion**. The test was performed in the range of T = +8 to -8 °C with constant shear conditions preset in the LVE region at γ = 0.1 % and ω = 10 rad/s. Evaluation of the functions of G' and G'' reveal typical behavior for a crystallizing material with G'' > G' above the **crystallization temperature** T_k and thus in a liquid state.

When reaching T_k = -1 °C, both G' and G'' rise steeply until finally G' > G'', indicating the frozen and thus solid state of the emulsion. Usually, the crystallization temperature of water is 0 °C. The slight

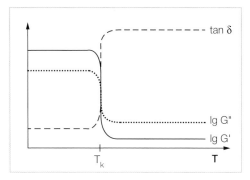

Figure 18.8: Temperature-dependent functions of G', G'' and tanδ for a crystallizing dispersion with the crystallization temperature T_k at the crossover point G' = G''

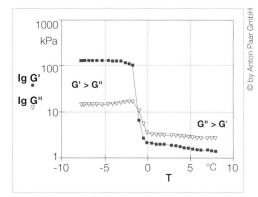

Figure 18.9: Temperature-dependent functions of G' and G'' during cooling of an emulsion with crystallization temperature T_k = -1 °C at the crossover point G' = G''

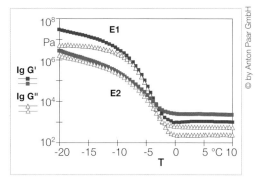

Figure 18.10: Comparison of the thermal behavior of two ice-cream samples E1 and E2 during heating, as temperature-dependent functions of G' and G''. At T = -20 °C, E2 is not as stiff as E1. E2 melts over a broader temperature range. In the molten state above T = 0 °C, E2 displays higher values of G' and G''.

shift is due to the fact that this sample is not pure water. In summary, it can be said that this lotion is certainly not appropriate for use as a sun-lotion base for alpine rambling in cool mountain winds or for skiing in cold winters.

Measuring example:
Comparison of the thermal behavior of two ice cream samples *(Figure 18.10)*.
The aim of the test was the comparison of two ice cream samples **upon warming** in the temperature range of $T = -20$ to $+10$ °C. Ice cream E1 was produced with a conventional freezer while a more advanced machine was used for ice cream E2. The test was performed under constant measuring conditions at $\gamma = 0.02$ % and $\omega = 10$ rad/s, with the temperature gradient $\Delta T/\Delta t = 1$ °C/min. For ice-cream consumers, the following three criteria are important from the application point of view.

1) At $T = -20$ °C, this is **when the ice cream is removed from the freezer**, the product should be solid, but not too stiff **for easy scooping and portioning (spoonability, dosability)**. E2 shows $G' > G''$ with $G' = 4$ MPa, and can thus easily be portioned, even with a plastic spoon. E1, on the other hand, shows $G' > G''$ with $G' = 40$ MPa, and thus the force needed is ten times higher. In this case, it is possible that even a metal spoon will bend when you try to scoop the sample if it is just out of the freezer.

2) In the range of $T = -20$ to 0 °C, when the samples start to melt, G' and G'' for E2 drop less steeply than for E1. This means that E2 has a broader softening range, thus allowing the **cold mouthfeel** to be perceived as **more pleasant**. In contrast, the relatively narrow melting range of sample E1 may result in a suddenly perceived and possibly painful coldness in the mouth.

3) At temperatures above 0 °C, both samples are molten and, with $G' > G''$, they have a **creamy texture** with $G' = 1$ kPa for E1 and $G' = 2$ kPa for E2. This means that the "thicker" E2 leads the consumers to believe that they have got a much richer ice cream for their money.

According to information provided by food technologists, these two ice creams differ mainly in the particle sizes of their ingredients i.e. air bubbles, highly viscous fat, oil droplets, solid particles and crystals. Their size is in the range of 0.1 to 10 µm. By using more advanced production technology, the bubbles, droplets and particles of sample E2 have a significantly lower average size than those of sample E1.

c) Tests performed at high temperatures
Specific measuring chambers are used for tests at high temperatures, for example in the range of $T = 450$ or 600 °C, or even up to 1000 °C, or 1800 °C *(Figure 18.11)*. The aim of such a test is to characterize thermal behavior during a **softening process** or upon **melting** of samples such as **glasses, metals** (e.g. aluminum, magnesium, alloys), **salts, slags** (e.g. from iron-ore smelting in blast furnaces for steelmaking), or **stone materials** (e.g. basalt).

Measuring example:
Thermal behavior of a glass sample *(Figure 18.12)*
The thermal behavior of a glass sample **during heating** in the range of T = 500 to 700 °C was tested. The test was performed using a plate/plate geometry equipped with plates of just 8 mm in diameter. Between 500 and 600 °C, this glass is in a solid state. The **glass temperature** or **glass-transition temperature T_g** is +612 °C, as evaluated at G'' maximum. At higher temperatures, the sample is molten, with G'' > G'.

The loss factor tanδ (= G''/ G') rises steadily without developing an intermediate maximum, as is seen with partially crystalline materials. This behavior is typical for materials with an amorphous structure. Rheologists working as materials researchers and physicists consider glass at a temperature below T_g to be an **amorphous solid** material, and not - as can still be read sometimes in chemistry books - a supercooled liquid.

Measuring example:
Determination of the glass temperature of glass samples *(Figure 18.13)*
The criterion a glass manufacturer applies to their glasses for quality control purposes is the glass temperature T_g, determined at G'' maximum.
The following values were determined: for G1: T_g = 334 °C, for G2: T_g = 378 °C, for G3: T_g = 568 °C, and for G4: T_g = 595 °C.

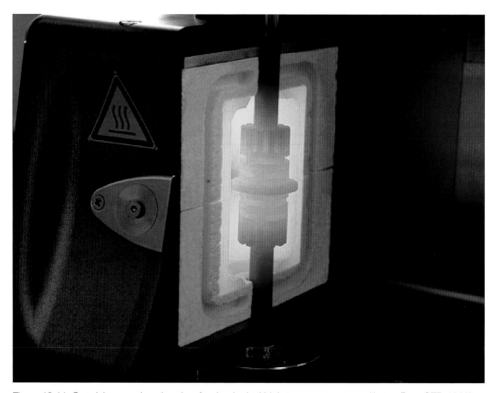

Figure 18.11: Special measuring chamber for rheological high-temperature tests (Anton Paar CTD 1000)

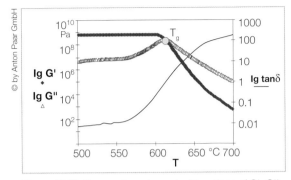

Figure 18.12: Temperature-dependent functions of G', G''
and tanδ of a glass sample during heating, with
$T_g = 612\ °C$ *at G'' maximum.*
A typical feature of the amorphous structure of glass is the
steadily increasing curve of loss factor tanδ.

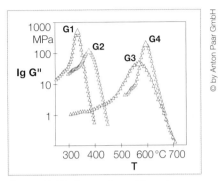

Figure 18.13: Comparison of four glass
samples based on the determination of the
glass-transition temperatures T_g at the
G'' maxima.

18.2 Temperature-dependent behavior with gel formation or curing

Typical tests in this field are aimed at investigating **behavior** during gel formation or
chemical curing **when a sample is heated**. Constant shearing is preset which means
that this oscillatory test is performed under **constant dynamic-mechanical conditions**.
For this test, the shear-strain (or shear-stress) amplitude, as well as the (angular)
frequency, are kept constant. In most cases, controlled-strain tests (or CSD, resp.) are
preferred. One disadvantage of controlled-shear-stress tests is that, with increasing
values of G' and G'', the extent of the resulting deformation of the sample will decrease
continuously.

In addition, a defined temperature profile is preset, usually with a temperature gradient
of 1 °C per minute. For this type of test, it is recommended that **disposable measuring
systems are used, consisting of a disposable plate and a disposable dish** for single
use (see *Figure 3.5*).

As a result, the temperature-dependent functions of G' and G'' are evaluated
(Figure 18.14).

The following three temperatures are of special interest:

a) Melting temperature T_m at the crossover point G' = G''; beyond this point the
sample is liquid.

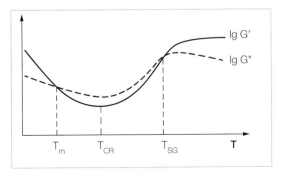

Figure 18.14:
Temperature-dependent functions of
G' and G'' of a material with gel
formation or chemical curing, with melting
temperature T_m at G' = G'' and T_{CR} at G'
minimum, indicating the beginning of a
gel-formation or curing process. In addition,
the sol/gel transition T_{SG} can be taken from
the second crossover point G' = G''.

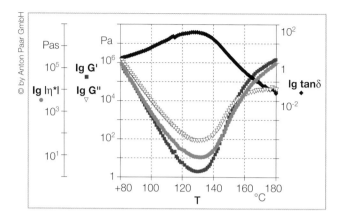

Figure 18.15:
Temperature-dependent functions of a powder coating during heating: G' and G'', tanδ and |η|. After softening, the curing process starts. The curing reaction begins at T_{CR} = 129 °C; i.e., at the minimum of the curves of G', G'' and |η*|, or at the maximum of tanδ.*
The sol/gel transition at T_{SG} = 153 °C occurs when G' = G'' or tanδ = 1.

b) Beginning of the gel formation or curing process at T_{CR}, for example in the form of a chemical reaction. At **G' or G'' minimum**, the values of G' and G'' – as well as the temperature at this point – are important. If these values are too high, a sample may not flow and level as well as desired; if these values are too low, problems such as edge failure of a coating may occur (e.g. with powder coatings).

c) Sol/gel transition T_{SG} at the second crossover point G' = G''; beyond this point the sample is solid.

Measuring example:

Temperature-dependent curing process of a powder coating *(Figure 18.15)*

This test was intended to describe the temperature-dependent behavior of a powder coating **when heated**. For the test, performed in the temperature range of T = +80 to +180 °C, a **disposable PP measuring system** was used. Preset were γ = 0.1 % and ω = 10 rad/s, both at constant values. After evaluation of the curves of G', G'', tanδ and |η*|, the following conclusions were drawn with regard to the **softening and curing process**:

a) At T = 80 °C, the powder coating is already in a molten state, because G'' > G' or tanδ = G''/ G' > 1.

b) The **beginning of the curing reaction** is at T_{CR} = 129 °C, which is the **minimum of the G' curve**. This is approximately the same temperature as at the minima of G'' and |η*|, as well as the maximum of tanδ, because of the maximal difference between G'' and G'.

c) The **sol/gel transition** is at T_{SG} = 153 °C at crossover point G' = G'' or at tanδ = 1. This point cannot be identified from only the |η*| curve, by the way; here the value of |η*| is 1050 Pas.

Conclusion:

Usually, the curves of G' und G'' are sufficient for evaluating the melting and curing behavior of a sample. The curve of tanδ is derived from these two functions, and does not provide any new or independent information. This is also true for the curve of |η*|. In practice, using the complex viscosity for evaluation makes sense only as long as the sample is in a liquid state, for example for determining the **viscosity minimum**. As far as this powder coating is concerned, the viscous behavior prevails in the temperature range from $T = 80$ °C up to the sol/gel transition, as only in this range is $G'' > G'$.

Measuring example:
Fusion and gel formation of plastisol
(Figure 18.16)
The behavior of a PVC plastisol was tested during heating in the temperature range from $T = +20$ to $+200$ °C. The measuring system used was a PP geometry with a gap width of $H = 1$ mm. Preset were $\gamma = 0.2$ % and $\omega = 10$ rad/s.
Plastisol is a blend of two phases. At ambient temperature it consists of two components; **polymer** as "polymer particles", which are suspended in the **plasticizer**, the latter consisting of comparably very small molecules (state 1 in *Figure 18.17*).

Whereas the polymer has a molar mass of more than 50,000 g/mol, the plasticizer's molar mass is only about 500 g/mol. In principle, the figure shows the process taking place during heating

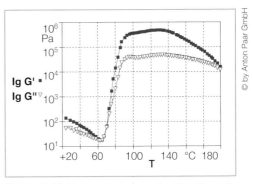

© by Anton Paar GmbH

Figure 18.16: Temperature-dependent functions of G' and G'' for a PVC plastisol during heating. After softening, the next stages are swelling, thickening and gelation.
Thickening starts at 65 °C after the minima of G' and G'' have been exceeded. Fusion of the two phases is complete at 95 °C. The drop in G' and G'' above 130 °C indicates that no chemical curing has taken place.

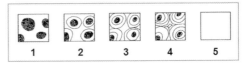

Figure 18.17: Plastisol as a two-phase mixture of polymer particles suspended in the plasticizer phase at ambient temperature (1). When heated, the polymer particles soften. Swelling is increasingly induced by the diffusion of the smaller plasticizer molecules into the polymer phase, resulting in an increased thickening of the mixture (2 to 4). Finally, a gel forms and the two phases fuse homogeneously (5).

when viewed with a **microscope**, for example **under cross-polarized light**. As can be seen from the curves of G' and G'', several process steps are performed during heating. Initially, at $T = 20$ °C the sample is pasty, with $G' = 150$ Pa and $G'' = 60$ Pa. This consistency can be compared to that of a hand cream.

After **softening, gelation begins** at $T = 65$ °C with a **swelling process** at the outer edges of the polymer particles, due to the plasticizer molecules starting to diffuse into the swelling polymer particles (state 2). At this point, the plastisol shows $G' \geq G''$ and it is therefore not correct to term this a molten state.
With a further increase in temperature, the plastisol continues to **thicken** (states 3 and 4). The small plasticizer molecules increasingly diffuse into the peripheral zones of the polymer phase. In doing so, these zones continue to swell until they touch each other. Finally, above about $T = 100$ °C, the two phases **fuse**, thus **forming a gel**. At this point, there is only a single homogeneous phase (state 5). This is the reason why no

boundaries are now visible between the phases under cross-polarized light. Here the values for G' and G'' are 600 kPa and 60 kPa, respectively.

Above T = 130 °C, G' and G'' start to decrease. This indicates that no chemical curing has taken place, and thus, there has been no formation of a rigid chemical network of primary bonds. Otherwise, when heating the sample further until reaching the point of thermal decomposition, the values would remain at a constantly high plateau value. At higher temperatures, the sample finally starts to soften, which continues as the temperature rises further. At T = 200 °C, G' and G'' have dropped to just 10 kPa each.

19. Torsional tests on solid samples

In principle, torsional tests are no different from the previously described sinusoidal oscillatory shear tests, except that they are carried out on solid materials.
In this chapter, we finally reach the right-hand side of Rheology Road, the "District of Solids".

Typical samples are solid **torsion bars** and **foils with a thickness of up to 1 mm** and a rectangular or circular cross section. They are fastened in a special **clamping fixture for solid bars**. The bottom clamp, for instance, is stationary, while the upper movable clamp is connected to the coupling of the measuring system and to the shaft of the rheometer drive *(Figures 19.1 and 19.2)*.

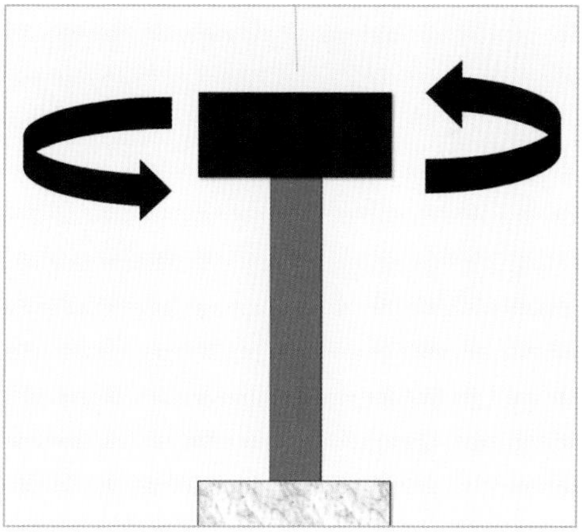

Typical dimensions of solid torsion bars with a rectangular cross section, for length, width and thickness are 40 x 10 x 1 (in mm). In fact, the entire test sample is slightly longer, because the dimension of 40 mm mentioned above only refers to the **free length between the two clamps**.

Other dimensions are also possible. For example, standard ISO 6721-2 states the following dimensions (in mm): (40 to 120) x (5 to 11) x (0.15 to 2).

© by Anton Paar GmbH

Figure 19.1: Bar-shaped sample for a torsional test with stationary bottom clamp and movable top clamp.

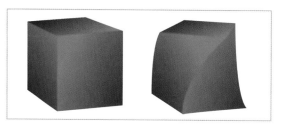

Figure 19.2: Principle of a torsional test, here shown with a cube-shaped sample. On the left, the viscoelastic material is at rest, whereas on the right it is deformed under torsional load. The bottom surface of the sample is stationary, while the upper part is twisted by an applied torsional force.

Tests with solid samples that are performed at a constant temperature are also called **dynamic-mechanical analysis** tests, or **DMA** in short. Tests carried out at varying measuring temperatures are called **dynamic-mechanical thermoanalysis** tests or **DMTA.**

DMA tests and DMTA tests are described **as torsional tests** in this chapter. In general, all tests with sinusoidal excitation are DMA or DMTA tests. This is true for almost all **oscillatory or vibrational tests** (according to ISO 6721-1). Examples:

a) Shear tests are carried out on viscoelastic liquids, semisolid and solid samples (as described in *Chapters 14 to 18*) and as **torsional tests** on solid samples (as described in this Chapter) in the form of **oscillation around a rotational axis** using the measuring parameters torque, angle of rotation and phase shift. For both types of tests, the rheological parameters G^*, G', G'' and $\tan\delta$ are determined.

b) Tensile tests as oscillatory tests involve the parameters tensile force, elongation and phase shift (as described in *Chapter 20*). With this type of test, the rheological parameters E^*, E', E'' and $\tan\delta$ are obtained.

c) Flexure or bending tests as oscillatory tests involve the parameters bending force, bending path and phase shift. Here again, the rheological parameters E^*, E', E'' and $\tan\delta$ are determined.

d) Compression tests as oscillatory tests involve the test parameters compression force, compression path and phase shift. The rheological parameters in these tests are the compression moduli and $\tan\delta$.

Measuring example:
Amplitude sweep of a glass-fiber-reinforced resin as a torsion bar
(Figures 19.3 and 19.4)
A glass-fiber-reinforced resin **as a composite material** in the shape of a torsion bar was tested at T = +20 °C. The dimensions of the sample, with a rectangular cross section were 50 x 10 x 1 (in mm), showing the free length of 50 mm between the clamps. The amplitude sweep was performed at an angular frequency of ω = 10 rad/s. This test is a **torsional DMA test** for solid specimen.

The evaluation showed in the LVE region 3.3 GPa = 3300 MPa as a plateau value for storage modulus G' and 0.022 GPa = 22 MPa for loss modulus G''. The loss factor is $\tan\delta = G''/ G' = 0.007$. The results, showing a **high G' value and a very low $\tan\delta$ of less than 0.01**, are typical for rigid solid materials. This means that the sample shows > 99 % **solid behavior** and < 1% viscous behavior. In practice, such behavior is called ideal-elastic. Furthermore, the very low limiting value of the LVE region of just

$\gamma = 0.02$ % is typical for the behavior of a very rigid solid material.

At higher strain values, G' drops slightly, whereas the loss modulus G'' rises more clearly, as can be seen in the logarithmic diagram. During the test, the sample is strained; i.e., **deformation energy is introduced into the material**. This energy is increasingly transformed into friction heat.

Initially, the glass fibers were firmly embedded in the polymer matrix. With progressing strain they detach more and more from the polymer fibers, with the result that **internal friction takes place locally**.

Consequently, friction heat warms up the sample, and the **friction energy** is thus used up in this way. The **rise in G''** reflects the increasing extent to which **energy is lost within the** sample **due to the energy transformation**.

This result can be seen as the **beginning of micro crack formation**, which ultimately, with increasing deformation, can result in material failure.

Measuring example:
Comparison of the thermal behavior of two laminates *(Figure 19.5).*

In the test, two laminates L1 and L2 are compared during heating in the temperature range between T = +30 and 180 °C. L1 was a non-modified and L2 a reinforced laminate. Both had been developed to be used as a **base for industrial flooring**. The objective was to ensure a certain firmness, even at higher temperatures, in order to prevent the material from softening too quickly, for example in the case of fire. The laminate samples were tested as **torsion bars** with dimensions 50 x 10 x 1 (in mm) to

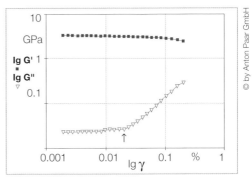

© by Anton Paar GmbH

Figure 19.3: Amplitude sweep of a glass-fiber-reinforced resin shaped as a torsion bar at T = +20 °C. The limit of the LVE region is reached at $\gamma = 0.02$ %. Beyond that, G'' rises due to the formation of micro cracks.

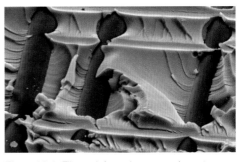

Figure 19.4: Fiber-reinforced epoxy-resin system viewed under an electron microscope. The individual fibers are embedded in the polymer matrix. Even at a certain deformation, sufficiently high adhesion between the two components of the composite material should be ensured [2].

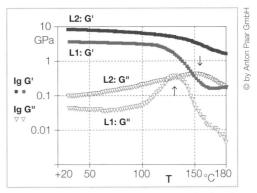

© by Anton Paar GmbH

Figure 19.5: Comparison of the thermal behavior of two laminates as torsion bars within the range of T = +30 to 180 °C. L1 was a non-modified and L2 a reinforced-composite material. At T = 30 °C, L1 shows G' = 4 GPa and L2 shows G' = 8 GPa. T_g at G'' maximum is 132 °C for L1 and 152 °C for L2.

be fixed at a free length of 50 mm between the clamps. The test was performed under constant dynamic-mechanical conditions at $\gamma = 0.01$ % and $\omega = 10$ rad/s. This means that this test is a typical **torsional DMTA test**.

Evaluation at T = 30 °C showed G' > G'' for both laminates, with G' being about one hundred times higher than G''. Both samples were very stiff solids, with G' = 4 GPa for L1 and G' = 8 GPa for L2.

For comparison: At ambient temperature, steel with G' = 80 GPa is just ten times stiffer than this **fiber-reinforced polymer composite**.

The **glass-transition temperature T_g** was determined via **G'' maximum**. The results were T_g = 132 °C for L1 and T_g = 152 °C for L2. The modification of the laminate was aimed at increasing T_g. Thus it was quite successful, with no less than ΔT = 20 °C. Moreover, the shapes of the G'' curves of L1 show typical behavior for **single-component materials**, with a clearly pronounced curve peak and steep slopes on each side. In contrast, the **multicomponent material** L2 shows flatter curve slopes and, correspondingly, a less-distinct maximum.

20. Tensile tests on polymer melts, films and foils

Apart from shear tests and torsional tests, which have already been described, tensile tests can deliver important additional information on the rheological behavior of materials.

The sample is fixed between two clamps; for example, one of the clamps is stationary while the other one can be moved in axial direction *(Figure 20.1)*. An alternative test method is the use of two counter-rotating drums for stretching a sample that has been fixed to both drums *(Figure 20.2)*. This kind of test can be conducted as a **rotational test** or as an **oscillatory test** (around a rotational axis).

20.1 Extensional viscosity

Besides the above-mentioned shear viscosity tests, **rotational tests** can also be performed to determine the **extensional viscosity of highly viscous and viscoelastic liquids**. Special measuring systems are used for this. Typical applications include **polymer melts** at a constant measuring temperature in the range of the glass-transition temperature T_g. Usually the extensional-strain rate is preset, and the function of extensional viscosity evaluated.

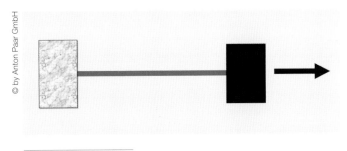

Figure 20.1:
Uniaxial and linear tensile test, here with a stationary and a moveable clamp.

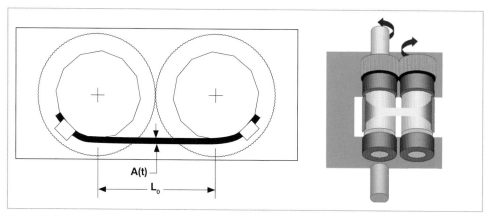

Figure 20.2: Stretching of the fixed sample by two counter-rotating drums. This is a rotational test (example: SER measuring system, Sentmanat extensional rheology system), with initial length L_0 and cross-sectional area A of the sample.

Definition of terms:

a) Tensile stress

Definition: $\sigma = F / A$

with tensile stress σ (pronounced: *sigma*), tensile force F (in N) and cross-sectional area A of the sample (in m^2)

The **unit for tensile stress** is 1 N/m^2 = **1 Pa (pascal)**.

The tensile stress is calculated by the analysis software. The following data are required for the calculation: The rheometer records the tensile force, or torque, at each measuring point. This torque is either preset or, if the extensional-strain rate is the preset value, it is determined via the tensile-resistance force of the sample.

After the user has entered the dimensions of the sample, with a rectangular cross section such as width b (in m) and thickness a (in m), into the analysis program, the software calculates the corresponding cross-sectional area of the sample:

A (in m^2) = b $\cdot$ a

For samples with a circular cross section, the following holds: $A = \pi \cdot (d^2/4)$, with diameter d (in m) and circle constant $\pi = 3.142$

b) Extensional-strain rate

A simplified definition of the extensional-strain rate is: $\dot{\varepsilon} = \dot{\varepsilon}_H = \varepsilon_H / t$

with extensional-strain rate $\dot{\varepsilon}$ (pronounced: *epsilon dot*), **Hencky strain rate** $\dot{\varepsilon}_H$,
Hencky strain ε_H (unit: 1 = 100 %), named after the physicist H. Hencky (1885 to 1951), and time t (in s)

The following holds: $\varepsilon_H = \ln(L/L_0)$ with initial free length of the sample L_0 (in m) and free length L (in m) during the test; "ln" is the natural logarithm to the base e (Euler's number). This definition is due to the exponential change of the sample's cross section caused by necking of the sample during the extension process.

The **unit for the extensional-strain rate** is **1/s = 1 s⁻¹** or "reciprocal seconds".

The extensional-strain rate is calculated by the analysis software. The following data are required for the calculation: The rheometer records the velocity of the change in length, or the rotational speed, at each measuring point. This speed is either preset or, if the tensile force is the preset value, it is determined via the extensional velocity of the sample. The free initial length L_0 of the sample is known at the beginning of the test.

c) Extensional viscosity
Definition: $\eta_E = \sigma / \dot{\varepsilon}$
with extensional viscosity η_E, tensile stress σ (in Pa) and extensional-strain rate $\dot{\varepsilon}$ (in s⁻¹)
This is the **Law of Viscosity for tensile testing**, often also called "Newton's Law". The **unit for extensional viscosity is 1 Pas = 1000 mPas (pascal seconds, milli-pascal seconds)**. Other units include
1 kPas = 1,000 Pas (kilo-Pas), 1 MPas = 1,000,000 Pas (mega-Pas).

For polymers in the region of the plateau value of zero-shear viscosity, and if the extensional-strain rate is the same as the shear rate, the **Trouton ratio** for extensional viscosity and shear viscosity holds: $\eta_E(\dot{\varepsilon}) = 3 \cdot \eta(\dot{\gamma})$

Measuring example:
Extensional behavior of a linear polymer *(Figure 20.3)*
The test sample was a high-density polyethylene (HDPE) consisting of **linear macro-molecules**. HDPE is used for bottle crates, garbage bins, gas tanks for cars, as well as for rigid pressure pipes and fittings for potable water supplies.

The sample was prepared as a platelet with dimensions 16 x 11 x 1 (in mm), and was fixed to both drums of the tensile measuring system. The free initial length between the two clamps was 12.2 mm.

Following a temperature-equilibration period of t = 5 min at the measuring temperature of T = 150 °C, the first test interval involved pre-stressing the sample for 5 s at a torque of M = 10 µNm. This sample preparation is necessary to prevent the material from sagging due to gravitational force. Under these conditions, the HDPE was in a highly viscous **rubber-elastic state** and could be described as a viscoelastic **polymer melt**.
Each of the three tests was performed with a new sample. In the second test interval, a constant extensional-strain rate (ER) $\dot{\varepsilon}$ was preset at 10 s⁻¹ for the first sample, at 1 s⁻¹ for the second, and

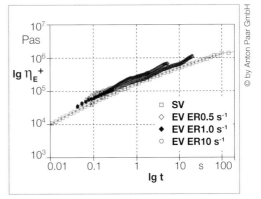

© by Anton Paar GmbH

Figure 20.3: Extensional behavior of an HDPE sample at T = 150 °C, with the growth curves of the time-dependent extensional viscosity η_E (EV) at three different extensional-strain rates (ER). The figure shows typical behavior for a linear polymer because the EV curves are almost congruent with the shear viscosity's growth curve (SV).

at 0.5 s^{-1} for the third. The drums were rotated by a maximum total angle of 450°. This means that each of the two counter-rotating drums was rotated by 225°. With any further rotation, the clamps would have touched each other and distorted the result.

For evaluation, a diagram with the so-called **growth curves of the time-dependent extensional viscosity** (EV) η_E^+ was plotted. The plus sign indicates that extensional viscosity is not constant but, rather, changes over time because there are still **start-up effects**.

The diagram also shows the growth curve of the time-dependent shear viscosity η^+ for this sample (SV, white squares), which was calculated from previously performed oscillatory shear tests. For comparison of the extensional viscosity curves, the shear viscosity is tripled in this plot, because the Trouton ratio applies: $\eta_E^+ = 3 \cdot \eta^+$

All three EV curves superimpose the SV growth curve so perfectly that they can hardly be distinguished. The higher the extensional-strain rate, the earlier the maximum angle of rotation is reached and, with that, the end of the test. After t = 10 s, the value of approximately $\eta_E^+ = 700$ kPas has been reached.

Measuring example:
Extensional behavior of a branched polymer *(Figure 20.4)*
The test sample was a low-density polyethylene (LDPE) consisting of **branched macromolecules**. The measuring conditions were the same as those used in the example above: Sample dimensions (16 x 11 x 1, in mm), free initial length (12.2 mm), measuring temperature (T = 150 °C), temperature-equilibration time (5 min), period of time and extent of pre-stressing in the first test interval (5 s at M = 10 µNm), maximum angle of rotation of the drums (450°), sample in a rubber-elastic state.

For each of the seven tests performed during the second test interval on the LDPE, a constant extensional-strain rate (ER) of $\dot{\varepsilon}$ = 20 / 10 / 5.0 / 1.0 / 0.5 / 0.1 and 0.01 s^{-1} was preset. As for the example above, a diagram showing the growth curve of shear

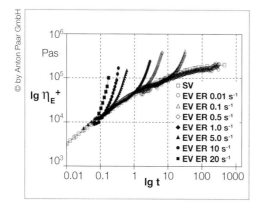

© by Anton Paar GmbH

Figure 20.4: Extensional behavior of an LDPE sample at T = 150 °C, with growth curves of the time-dependent extensional viscosity η_E (EV) at seven different extensional-strain rates (ER). The figure shows typical behavior for a branched polymer because six of the EV curves measured at higher extensional rates rise more steeply at the end than the shear viscosity's growth curve (SV).

viscosity η^+ (SV curve with white squares) and the time-dependent curves of **extensional viscosity** (EV) η_E^+ was used for evaluation.
The higher the extensional-strain rate (ER), the earlier the maximum angle of rotation is reached and, with that, the end of the test.

The sample shows **strain-hardening** because six of the EV curves have steeper slopes than the growth curve at the end. Only the EV curve obtained at a very low extensional-strain rate of 0.01 s^{-1} follows the SV growth curve to the end. After t = 10 s, the value of approximately η_E^+ = 100 kPas has been reached; this is clearly less than for the HDPE sample, with η_E^+ = 700 kPas.

This is why branched polymers such as LDPE are often used as a flexible packaging material in the form of foils, tote bags, cable sheathing and also for bottles, cans, containers and pipes. With their strain-hardening properties, extensive deformation should be avoidable, while rupture and final fracture should at least be postponed.
Remark: Linear polymers can also display strain-hardening; in particular, polymers with a high molar mass.

20.2 Tensile modulus and elastic behavior
This section deals with the description of slow **rotational tests** (used to determine the **tensile behavior of solid films and foils, as well as of highly viscous, viscoelastic liquids**) conducted with special measuring systems. Typical experiments are performed on **polymer films (up to a maximum thickness of 0.25 mm) and foils (up to 1 mm)**.

Definition of terms:
a) **Tensile stress**: see *Chapter 20.1a*

b) **Extensional strain (or elongation)**
Definition: $\varepsilon = \varepsilon_H = \ln(L/L_0)$
with extensional strain ε (pronounced: *epsilon*), **Hencky strain** ε_H (see *Chapter 20.1b*)
The **unit for extensional strain** is (m/m) = 1, i.e., it is **dimensionless**; usually it is stated as a percentage. The following holds: 1 = 100%

The extensional strain is calculated by the analysis software. The following data are required for the calculation: The rheometer records the path, or the deflection angle at each measuring point. This angle is either preset or, if the tensile force is the preset value, it is determined via the deformation of the sample.
The free initial length L_0 of the sample is known at the beginning of the test.

c) **Tensile modulus, elasticity modulus or E modulus, or Young's modulus**
Definition: E = σ / ε
with tensile modulus E, tensile stress σ (in Pa) and extensional strain ε
(with the unit: 1 = 100%)
This is the **Law of Elasticity for tensile testing**, often also called Hooke's Law.

The **unit of the tensile modulus** is **1 Pa (pascal)**. Other units are:
1 GPa (giga-pascal) = 1000 MPa (mega-pascal) = 10^6 kPa (kilo-pascal) = 10^9 Pa.
Explanation: The higher the E value, the stiffer the material. The Law of Elasticity can be compared with the Law of Springs for tensile springs and compression springs (see *Figure 12.7*):
C = F / s, with spring force F, deflection path s, and spring constant C, which describes the stiffness of a spring.

For correlating the values of the tensile modulus E and the shear modulus G, the following applies:
E = 2 · G (1 + μ), with Poisson's ratio μ
Poisson's ratio is a dimensionless number that describes the ratio of transverse deformation to axial deformation. E.g., for a sample with a circular diameter:
$\mu = (\Delta d \cdot L_0) / (d_0 \cdot \Delta L)$
with $\Delta d = d_0$ - d and $\Delta L = L - L_0$, initial sample diameter d_0 (in m) and diameter d (in m) during the test, as well as with free initial length L_0 (in m) and free length L (in m) during the test.

Since $0 \le \mu \le 0.5$, for all kinds of materials the following holds: **E = (2 to 3) · G**
The values for stiff and brittle materials, such as solids, are closer to factor 2
(or $\mu = 0$), **while the values for liquid materials, such as polymer melts, are closer to factor 3** (or $\mu = 0.5$).

Measuring example:
Temperature-dependent extensional behavior of a coating film *(Figure 20.5)*
The tensile behavior of a **80 μm thin polymer film** was examined at different temperatures with a focus on the region of the glass-transition temperature T_g = +90 °C. The figure shows the different **tensile stress/extensional strain (elongation) curves** of the film. At T = +20 °C, the material is stiff and displays **brittle fracture behavior** (1). At 80 °C, which is still below T_g, and after a certain elongation with a high initial stiffness, the film finally shows **cold flow** (2). At T = +100 °C, the sample displays **rubber-elastic behavior**, with little stiffness and a high degree of stretchability, before - after a very

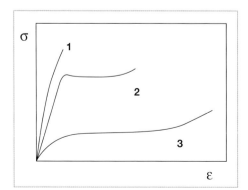

Figure 20.5: Tensile stress/elongation curves
(σ / ε) of a polymer film at different measuring temperatures.
(1) Stiff behavior with low stretchability and brittle fracture in the cold state clearly below T_g
(2) Cold flow a little below T_g
(3) Rubber-elastic behavior with a high degree of stretchability at $T > T_g$ showing strain hardening finally.

pronounced **strain-hardening** - it finally ruptures (3). The strain-hardening behavior can be clearly seen by the curve bending upwards at the end.

20.3 Extensional rheology with oscillatory tests

This section deals with the description of **oscillatory tests** used to determine the **extensional behavior of films (up to a maximum thickness of 0.25 mm) and foils (up to 1 mm) as well as of highly viscous and viscoelastic liquids**. Special measuring systems are used for these kinds of tests.

In general, oscillatory tests conducted at constant temperature are also called **dynamic-mechanical analysis tests or DMA tests**. Tests carried out at varying temperature are called **dynamic-mechanical thermoanalysis tests or DMTA tests**.

DMA tests and DMTA tests are described as tensile tests in this chapter. Apart from this type of test, there are also shear tests and torsional tests (as described in *Chapters 14 to 19*) as well as bending tests and compression tests. Typical DTMA tests, for example, are used for describing thermal behavior over a wide temperature range and, in particular, for determining the **glass-transition temperature** T_g of polymer films and foils. Usually, the test is performed under **constant dynamic-mechanical conditions**, i.e., at constant amplitude as well as constant (angular) frequency.

The definitions of the measured and analyzed values for oscillatory tensile tests are similar to the values G^*, G', G'' and $\tan\delta$ from shear tests and torsional tests.

a) Complex tensile modulus E^*

Definition of the **Law of Elasticity for oscillatory tensile tests:**

$$E^* = \sigma_A / \varepsilon_A$$

Complex tensile modulus E^* (E star, in Pa) describes the entire viscoelastic behavior. The index A stands for the amplitude of the sine curves of both the tensile stress σ and the extensional strain ε.

b) **The storage modulus E'** (E prime, in Pa) **or storage modulus in tension** represents the elastic portion of the viscoelastic behavior, which essentially describes the solid-state behavior of a sample. Alternative term: elastic modulus in tension.

c) **The loss modulus E''** (E double prime, in Pa) **or loss modulus in tension** characterizes the viscous portion of the viscoelastic behavior, which reflects the liquid-state behavior of a sample. Alternative term: viscous modulus in tension.

d) **The loss factor or damping factor $\tan\delta$**

Definition of the loss factor or damping factor in tension: **$\tan\delta = E''/ E'$** (tangent delta), unit: dimensionless (or 1).

This parameter describes the ratio of the two portions of the viscoelastic behavior.

(1) For **ideal-elastic behavior** with no viscous portion and therefore with $E'' = 0$, $\delta = 0°$ and $\tan\delta = 0$.

(2) For **ideal-viscous behavior** with no elastic portion and therefore with $E' = 0$, $\delta = 90°$, and $\tan\delta$ approaches infinity.

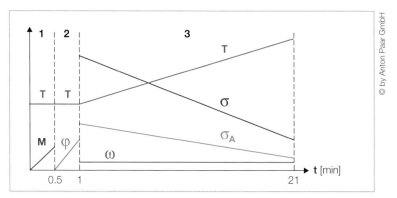

© by Anton Paar GmbH

Figure 20.6: Preset for testing the thermal-extensional behavior of three paint films, performed in three test intervals, with temperature T, torque M during pre-stressing, angle of rotation φ during pre-straining, as well as tensile stress σ (rotation), tensile-stress amplitude σ_A (oscillation) and angular frequency ω. This DMTA test was carried out as a rotational test with superimposed oscillation.

Measuring example:
Comparison of the thermal extensional behavior of three coating films using DMTA tests performed as a rotational test with superimposed oscillation

The **glass-transition temperatures** T_g were determined for three **paint films**. The film samples had the following dimensions for length, width and thickness: 19 x 10 x 0.044 (in mm). The films, each with a thickness of 44 μm, were fixed between the two drums of the extensional measuring system.

The first two test intervals were carried out for sample preparation of the actual DTMA measurement in order to prevent sagging of the thin paint films *(Figure 20.6)*:
(1) **Pre-stressing** for t = 30 s at T = +20 °C with torque increasing from M = 0 to 1 mNm (as rotation).
(2) **Pre-straining** for t = 30 s at T = +20 °C with angle of rotation increasing from φ = 0 to 1° (as rotation).
Next, the third test interval involved **presetting the tensile stress as rotation with superimposed oscillation**:
(3) **Preset of the temperature** by heating from T = +20 °C to 120 °C with a temperature gradient of ΔT/Δt = 5 °C/min, as well as **rotation** with the tensile stress decreasing from σ = 1000 kPa to 10 kPa **and simultaneously superimposed oscillation**, with the tensile-stress amplitude decreasing from σ_A = 400 kPa to 4 kPa, at a constant angular frequency of ω = 10 s⁻¹. Continuous reduction of the tensile stress was necessary because the films softened continuously during heating.

Evaluation showed that, in the beginning at T = 20 °C, there were only minor differences between the three films with E' values between 300 and 400 MPa, and with tanδ = E''/ E' = 0.03 to 0.05 *(Figure 20.7)*. However, the **values of T_g** differ clearly. They were determined via **the maxima of the E'' functions.** The results were T_g= 57 °C for film 1, T_g = 69 °C for film 2 and T_g = 76 °C for film 3.

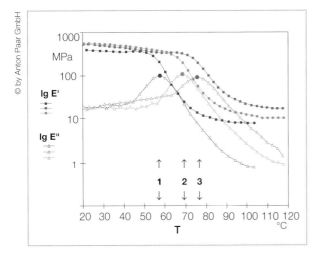

Figure 20.7:
Comparison of three paint films via
tensile DMTA tests in the temperature
range from T = +20 °C to +120 °C,
presented with the curves of the storage
modulus E' and the loss modulus E''.
The values of T_g at the maximum of
each E'' curve are
57 °C for film 1,
69 °C for film 2
and 76 °C for film 3.

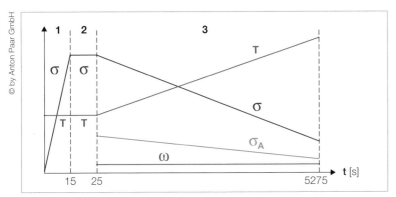

Figure 20.8: Preset for testing the thermal-extensional behavior of a multi-layer film, performed in three test intervals, with temperature T and tensile stress σ (rotation) during pre-stressing as well as during the DMTA test carried out as a rotational test with superimposed oscillation, the latter with tensile-stress amplitude $σ_A$ (oscillation) and angular frequency ω.

Measuring example:
Thermal extensional behavior of a multi-layer film (e.g., used as a packaging material)
The region of the glass-transition temperatures of a **composite film** were determined.
The multi-layer film with a **total thickness of 35 μm** was a **co-extrudate** consisting of
the two components poly methyl methacrylate (PMMA) and polycarbonate (PC).

The first two test intervals were carried out for sample preparation of the actual DTMA
measurement, in order to prevent sagging of the thin film *(Figure 20.8)*:
(1) **Pre-stressing** for t = 15 s at T = +25 °C, with the tensile stress increasing from
σ = 0 to 5 MPa (as rotation).
(2) **Pre-stressing** for t = 10 s at T = +25 °C, with a constant tensile stress of
σ = 5 MPa (as rotation).

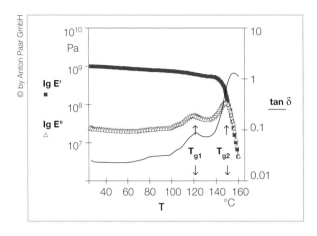

Figure 20.9: Thermal behavior of a multi-layer film in tensile DMTA tests in the range of $T = +25$ to 160 °C, plotted as curves of E' and E'' as well as loss factor $\tan\delta$. The two components of the composite film show $T_{g1} = 120$ °C for the PMMA layer and $T_{g2} = 149$ °C for the PC layer, both determined at the maximum of E''.

Next, the third test interval was performed by **presetting the tensile stress as rotation with superimposed oscillation:**

(3) **The temperature was preset** by heating from $T = +25$ °C to 200 °C with a temperature gradient of $\Delta T/\Delta t = 2$ °C/min. **The rotation** was also preset, with the tensile stress decreasing from $\sigma = 5$ MPa to 0.05 MPa, **as was the simultaneously superimposed oscillation** with tensile-stress amplitudes decreasing from $\sigma_A = 1$ MPa to 0.01 MPa at a constant angular frequency of $\omega = 10$ s^{-1}. Continuous reduction of tensile stress was necessary because the films softened increasingly during heating.

The following **two glass-transition temperatures** were determined via the two E'' maxima *(Figure 20.9)*: $T_{g1} = 120$ °C for PMMA and $T_{g2} = 149$ °C for PC.

21. Tips for avoiding measuring errors

In this chapter, Joe Flow would like to advise you on how to recognize and avoid typical measuring errors.

One prerequisite for meaningful measurements is a well-calibrated instrument. The term "measured value" used in the following text predominantly refers to torque or shear stress, as well as to viscosity, storage modulus G' and loss modulus G''.

1) Selecting the optimal geometry of the measuring geometry
Give careful consideration to the selection of the measuring geometry (*Chapter 3.1* and *Figure 3.2*).

Joe Flow says:
As a rule of thumb when testing dispersions, the measuring gap should be at least ten times larger than the maximum size of the particles or solid agglomerates in the sample *(Chapter 3.1a).* If you do not observe this rule, your measured values may be too high.

a) Cone/plate (CP) or cone-and-plate measuring geometries
CP are suitable **for most samples.** However, there is a limiting factor: Because the shear gap at the center of the cone is usually very narrow, the rule of thumb regarding maximum particle size, as mentioned above by Joe Flow, is particularly important with this kind of geometry systems.

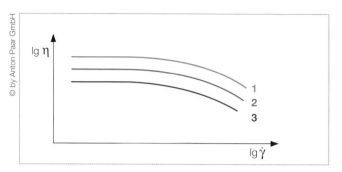

© by Anton Paar GmbH

Figure 21.1:
Shear-rate dependent viscosity functions:
(1) Proper test with a correctly set measuring gap,
(2) gap too small, wall-slip effects may have a stronger influence,
(3) gap too large, only part of the sample will be sheared.

b) Concentric-cylinder (CC) measuring geometries

CC geometries are recommended **for low-viscosity liquids and liquids with low surface tension** (such as oils), because they often tend to flow out of the gap of CP or PP geometries. **Samples that dry quickly** should also be measured with a CC geometry because the annular shear gap of a CC is covered from above by a thick layer of excess sample.

c) Plate/plate or parallel plates (PP) measuring geometries

PP geometries are well suited for **samples that contain comparably larger particles** because here, the typical PP gap width of 0.5 to 1.0 mm is rather large.

Highly viscous samples, such as unfilled polymer melts, are mostly tested with a PP geometry. In a CP geometry, the samples are subjected to much more shearing (stress and strain) during gap setting because of the much smaller gap. Thus, in a CP geometry, polymer samples would need a significantly longer relaxation time prior to the actual measurement.

PP geometries are recommended **for tests performed in a variable temperature range**. Due to the larger measuring gap, there is the advantage that the thermal expansion of measuring geometry and sample are less noticeable (than with CP).

Please note:
Make sure that the zero gap setting is performed correctly when using CP or PP geometries. With modern rheometers, the control program will take care of this. If the measuring gap is too small, testing will be influenced to a higher degree by wall-slip effects, resulting in measured values that are too low. If the gap is too large, only a part of the sample will be sheared, which also results in measured values that are too low.
(Figure 21.1).

2) Pretreatment and resting time for the sample prior to testing

The history of the sample is important and should always be taken into consideration. This applies to **all mechanical, thermal and temporal stresses** that the sample has experienced prior to testing.

> **Joe Flow says:**
> Make sure that the sample is homogeneous; for example, free of air bubbles. For achieving comparable values, it is advisable to prepare each sample using the same method. For example, storage conditions and stirring processes should be standardized. In general, stirring or shaking should be avoided; however, if it is unavoidable, make sure that it is always performed in the same way.

The procedures of putting the sample into the measuring system and setting the measuring gap already place stress on the sample. If the subsequent **time-dependent regeneration of the sample's inner structure** takes a longer time, a corresponding **recovery time** must be incorporated prior to starting the measurement (thixotropic behavior, *Chapters 9.1* and *17.1*). Too short a recovery time results in incorrect values; for example, in *Figure 21.2* the viscosity measured for sample 2 is too low, and the curves show the shape of a **growth curve** because there are still **start-up effects.**

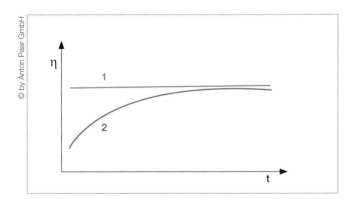

© by Anton Paar GmbH

Figure 21.2:
Measurement of the time-dependent viscosity curves of two samples for assessing the time the samples need to rebuild their structure after previous shearing, here as a controlled-shear-rate test at 1 s⁻¹:
Sample 1 does not need a resting time before the measurement; in contrast, sample 2 requires a longer resting time because it shows a prolonged structural recovery.

> **Joe Flow says:**
> For samples that need a longer recovery time, a resting interval should be integrated into the test program prior to the first test interval; for example, for a period of one to five minutes, if needed. Furthermore, with modern rheometers, the stress on the sample can be reduced because the time required for gap setting can be adjusted accordingly.

3) Optimum sample quantity and trimming

When using a CP or PP geometry, if the sample quantity is too large, this results in measured values that are too high due to **overfilling** of the measuring gap, and vice versa in the case of **underfilling**.

Joe Flow says:
When using CP and PP geometries, it is advisable to trim the sample (see Chapter 3.1 **and** Figure 3.3**).**

4) Torque range and size of the measuring geometries

The tests should take place within the **optimum torque range**. It is desirable to work in a range that is greater than 10 times the minimum torque but less than 90 % of the maximum torque of the instrument used.

If a flow curve exceeds the constant **maximum shear stress** (or the maximum torque) of the measuring geometry used, the diagram will show a parallel line to the x-axis. In this case, a **measuring geometry with a smaller diameter** (or a smaller shear area) should be used.

If the measured values deviate strongly from the expected ranges of low shear rate (or rotational speed) or deformation (or deflection angle) and show marked outliers, then the **resulting shear-stress values** (or torque values) are often **too low**. In this case, a **measuring geometry with a larger diameter** should be used.

Joe Flow says:
A short test performed prior to the actual test will show whether the correct measuring geometry has been selected in terms of the upper and lower limiting-shear-stress values. The shear-stress range of the measuring geometry used is stated on the data sheet provided with each system.

5) Shear waves in low-viscosity liquids, e.g., measured with a CP or PP geometry at high frequencies (oscillation)

For oscillatory tests performed in the range of high frequencies, such as a frequency sweep, interfering side effects can be expected, in particular for **low-viscosity liquids** (with viscosities below 100 mPas; *Figure 21.3*).

A rheometer always detects the sum of two torques: On the one hand, there is the torque that is required to move the entire driving system of the rheometer, including the measuring geometry (e.g. CP or PP) used. However, this torque value can actively be compensated for, and thus, can be almost completely eliminated by a combination of optimized instrument design and intelligent motor control during the measurement (example: an electronically commutated synchronous drive). For this purpose, a simple pre-test is conducted, where the driving torque is determined with an empty measuring geometry (this means: filled with air).

On the other hand, there is the torque value that is measured as a result of the rheological behavior of the sample. Since this latter torque should be as large as possible relative to the driving torque of the rheometer (determined for the empty measuring geometry), using a measuring system with a shear area that is as large as possible would be effective.

Furthermore, low-viscosity samples develop a **fluid-specific inertia effect** that can be observed as so-called **shear waves in the shear gap** at high frequencies; these waves

Joe Flow says:

For frequency sweeps on low-viscosity liquids, select a CP or PP geometry with a diameter that is as large as possible (for example 50 mm) and a measuring gap that is as small as possible.
For a PP geometry, for example, this would mean a plate distance of 0.5 mm or even just 0.3 mm. For a CP geometry this would be a cone angle of 1° or 0.5°, or even just 0.3°.

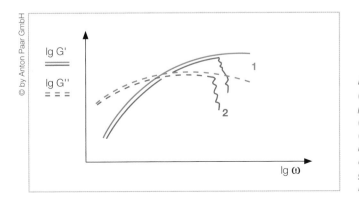

© by Anton Paar GmbH

Figure 21.3: Frequency sweep (oscillation) on an uncrosslinked polymer:
(1) good measurement,
(2) interfering effects occurring at high (angular) frequencies when using too small a measuring geometry or too wide a measuring gap.

arise because they are not able to follow the rapid motion without delay. This effect can be minimized by reducing the sample quantity. If the measuring gap is very narrow, this effect becomes negligible.

6) Wall-slip effects

For samples that contain oil or fat, **wall-slip effects** in the measuring geometry should be taken into account. In this case, the measured values will decrease earlier than usual and will continue to decrease. Often, **sandblasted or profiled surfaces** can prevent or at least delay this effect (*Chapter 3* with *Figure 3.4, Figure 21.4*).

Joe Flow says:
For samples containing oil or fat, and for samples which are otherwise difficult to measure in terms of wall-slip effects, comparison tests conducted with regular smooth surfaces, as well as with sand-blasted and profiled surfaces, will provide useful information on the occurrence and extent of this effect.

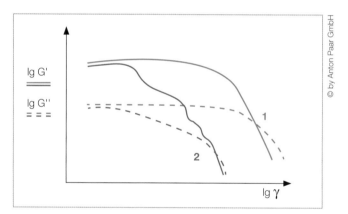

© by Anton Paar GmbH

Figure 21.4: Amplitude sweeps (oscillation) on a fat-containing sample:
(1) Good measurement without wall-slip effects when using a profiled plate.
(2) Wall-slip effects occurring at high shear-strain values when using a smooth plate. Therefore, here, the measured values fluctuate, decrease earlier and, for instance, the crossover point G' = G'' cannot be clearly defined.

7) Sufficient temperature equilibration of sample and measuring system

The temperature is the most important influencing factor for all rheological values. **Too short a temperature-equilibration time** (heating or cooling phase) will deliver incorrect results because the temperature will be not uniform throughout the entire sample. Too low a temperature increases the measured values and vice versa.

Joe Flow says:
Temperature-equilibration time prior to the measurement should be at least five, or even ten minutes, depending on the measuring temperature.

When **heating or cooling rates are too high**, the sample temperature will not comply with the target values. There will be a significant temperature difference at different locations in the measuring gap, producing a temperature gradient in the sample.

Measuring example:
The heating or cooling rate has a strong influence on the determination of specific temperature values, such as the glass-transition temperature T_g of a polymer, or the pour point of an oil *(Figure 21.5)*.

Joe Flow says:
For all rheometrical tests, heating rates and cooling rates of 1 °C/min and maximal 2 °C/min are recommended.

When conducting tests at temperatures that deviate by more than 10 °C from room temperature, as well as for tests performed in a range of variable temperature by heating or cooling (temperature sweeps), the use of an **"active" temperature control hood** is recommended *(Chapter 10)*. With such equipment, the temperature gradient can usually be reduced to a negligible minimum.

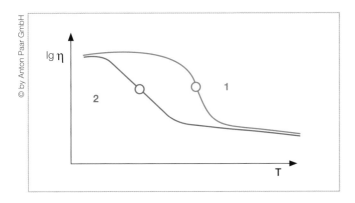

Figure 21.5: Temperature-dependent viscosity functions of a mineral oil during cooling for determination of the pour point:
(1) Good measurement at a cooling rate of 1 °C/min.
(2) The value determined for the pour point was too low because the cooling rate was too high to achieve a uniform temperature within the entire oil sample.

© by Anton Paar GmbH

8) Viscous-shear heating at very high shear rates

At very high shear rates (>1000 s^{-1}), maintaining a constant measuring temperature can be a challenge because the sample is also heated by the internal friction that develops during the flow process. In this case, the increase in the measured values would be slower than usual (in the case of shear stress) or they would decrease continuously (in the case of viscosity; *Figure 21.6*).

Please remember:
Every flowing liquid has a flow resistance that is produced by the internal friction of the molecules and, if present, also by other components of the liquid (*Chapter 1*). This is called viscous-shear heating.

Joe Flow says:
At high shear rates, it is advisable to preset a measuring duration that is as short as possible; for example, by selecting a small number of measuring points, and a measuring-point duration of just one second.

© by Anton Paar GmbH

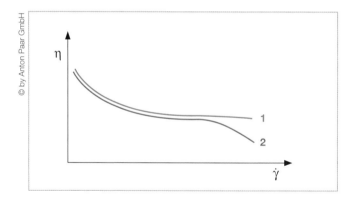

Figure 21.6: Shear-rate-dependent viscosity functions of a polymer solution:
(1) good measurement,
(2) too long a measuring-point duration at high shear rates. Here, due to viscous-shear heating, the viscosity decreases continuously.

9) Edge failure

When using a CP or PP geometry, edge failure should always be taken into consideration. Therefore, it is recommended that **the edge of the gap should always by watched** closely. For this purpose, a video camera can be used to record optical data such as images or videos.

a) Centrifugal force

When using a CP or PP geometry at high shear rates, inertia effects can cause the sample to flow out of the gap or even to be ejected, which results in continuously decreasing measured values *(Figure 21.7)*.

Joe Flow says:

For samples that tend to run out of the gap, select a measuring duration that is as short as possible.

© by Anton Paar GmbH

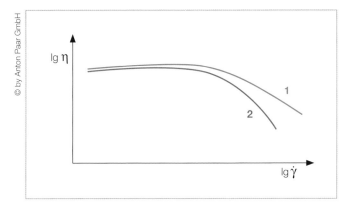

Figure 21.7: Shear-rate-dependent viscosity functions: (1) good measurement; the sample remained in the measuring gap, (2) poor measurement caused by loss of sample out of the gap.

b) Streak formation, shear fracture and melt fracture

At very high shear rates in CP and PP geometries, highly viscous and viscoelastic samples such as pastes and polymer melts may develop streaks and edge effects, including shear fracture and melt fracture (*Chapter 11* and *Figure 11.7*). This often results in the sample breaking transversally and parallel to the bottom plate, so that only part of the sample is still sheared. The sample no longer flows homogeneously, and **discharge of the sample from the gap** and **inclusion of air bubbles** can be expected. As a consequence, the measured values often fluctuate significantly, most commonly with a tendency to continuously decrease.

Joe Flow says:

For samples that show edge effects, it is advisable to select a measuring duration that is as short as possible.

10) Turbulent flow

At high shear rates, low-viscosity liquids (viscosity < 100 mPas) can develop **turbulent flow**, with so-called **secondary flow effects**, such as vortex formation (*Chapter 4* and *Figure 4.12*). In this case, the measured values will be significantly increased (*Figure 21.8*). If this happens, the requirement for laminar flow is no longer met, and therefore the measured values obtained can no longer be considered as being absolute values.

Joe Flow says:
Use measuring systems with a narrow gap for low-viscosity liquids; for example, a double-gap (DG) cylinder geometry, as the gap here is much narrower than in a standard cylinder geometry. Alternatively, a CP system with a small cone angle may be used (1° or 0.5° or even just 0.3°).

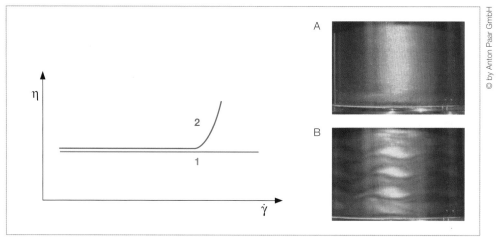

© by Anton Paar GmbH

Figure 21.8: Shear-rate-dependent viscosity functions of a low-viscosity dispersion containing gold-colored particles in acetone:
(1) good measurement, producing ideal-viscous flow behavior,
(2) with turbulent-flow behavior at high shear rates.
The measuring systems used were a double-gap (DG) geometry for (1) and a common concentric-cylinder (CC) geometry for (2). The pictures show laminar flow (A) and turbulent flow with vortices (B).

11) Rod climbing (Weissenberg effect)

When conducting rotational tests with a CC geometry, it may happen that, **at increased rotational speed** (or shear rate), viscoelastic liquids climb up the stirrer shaft. Rheologists call this the Weissenberg effect (*Chapter 11 and Figure 11.5*). It may result in an increasing amount of sample material migrating out of the annular gap between the cup and the bob. This effect can produce decreased measured values. Such effects can also occur in CP and PP geometries, leading to edge failure.

Joe Flow says:

When testing, observe the behavior of a sample, especially on uncovered surfaces or open shear gaps, in order to limit the maximum shear rate, if necessary.

12) Start-up effects and transient effects

Transient (time-dependent) effects can occur if the measuring-point duration is too short for tests made **in the range of low shear rates** (e.g. below 1 s^{-1}). These effects are also called start-up effects (producing growth curves) because the flow within the entire measuring gap has not yet completely adapted to the preset shear conditions. In this case, the calculated values will be too low. For a sample with shear-thinning behavior, within the course of the measurement, often a **transient viscosity maximum** (or peak) develops (see *Chapter 8.3, Figures 8.5* and *8.6*).

Joe Flow says:

There is a rule of thumb that should be followed for tests in the low shear range ($\dot{\gamma} < 1$ s^{-1}):
The duration for each measuring point (t$_{MP}$) should correspond at least to the reciprocal shear-rate value, which is t$_{MP} \geq (1 / \dot{\gamma})$.
It is better to select fewer measuring points for each shear rate decade and to provide a sufficient period of time for each individual measuring point instead.

13) Segregation of the sample

Physically unstable samples consisting of components with different densities may segregate due to gravitational force. This can be experienced as **sedimentation (settling) of particles, flotation (creaming) of droplets or syneresis** (segregation of different phases). Often such separation develops as a **long-term effect**.

> **Joe Flow says:**
> **If the sample segregates prior to the test, it should be homogenized, for example by stirring. If segregation occurs during the test, reduce the measuring time.**

Alternatively, **measuring geometries in the form of stirrers** can be used (see *Chapter 2* and *Figure 2.7*, relative measuring geometries). If using such a system, please bear in mind that the measured values are no longer absolute values but, rather, relative values. This is because, on the one hand, the measuring geometry no longer complies with the specifications for absolute measuring geometries and, on the other hand, because there is no longer laminar flow, but **turbulent flow**.

14) Evaporation of solvents, and drying out of the sample

For samples that contain water or another solvent that can evaporate, the use of a CC geometry is recommended because other measuring systems can lead to drying out of, or **skin formation** on, the sample. Since with CC geometries, a certain excess sample is used when filling the cup, the influence of the above-mentioned effects on the test result is minimal, in particular when using an additional **hood** or **solvent trap**.

Thus, a solvent trap should be used for CP and PP geometries. A suitable design with a liquid reservoir that can be filled with solvent or water ensures that the measuring space is sealed from the environment. In this case, the sample is surrounded by a more-or-less **saturated atmosphere**. If the sample dries out, the measured values will usually increase steadily over time *(Figure 21.9)*.

> **Joe Flow says:**
> **Use a hood and a measuring system with solvent trap for samples that tend to dry out or evaporate.**

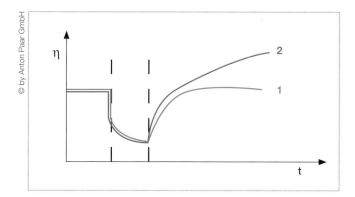

© by Anton Paar GmbH

Figure 21.9: Step test with three intervals (low shear/high shear/ low shear) for determination of the time-dependent structural recovery of a sample in the third test interval:
(1) Good measurement with partial regeneration, or thixotropic behavior of the sample.
(2) The measured values increase over time because the sample is drying out.

15) Thermal expansion or contraction of torsion bars

When **heating** a solid bar in a torsional test *(Chapter 19)*, **thermal expansion** can deform the bar, which is fixed between two clamps. This thermal expansion can thus lead to **compressive stress, upsetting deformation, bending** and finally **buckling** of the sample.

Correspondingly, **cooling** can cause **shrinking** of a sample due to **thermal contraction,** resulting in **tensile stress, extensional strain, stretching, elongation** and, finally, **rupture** of the sample.

It is obvious that these effects will have a significant influence on the test results, in particular if the sample shows **anisotropic properties**, which means that its behavior is direction-dependent.

Joe Flow says:
For achieving good results in tests with solid torsion bars, use a rheometer that allows the distance between the clamps to be set and controlled automatically.

22. The end of the stroll along Rheology Road

Your stroll along Rheology Road from the "District of Liquids" to the "District of Solids" has finally come to an end.

During your journey you were introduced most notably to the viscous, viscoelastic and elastic properties of different materials and how they can be influenced by:

- external forces (or shear stress or tensile stress)
- extent of deformation (or shear strain or extensional strain)
- strain velocity (or shear rate or extensional-strain rate)
- duration of shearing (and in the case of thixotropic behavior, possibly also the duration of the subsequent period of rest)
- temperature (e.g. from $T = -150$ to $+1800\ °C$)

Beyond that, there are many more rheological parameters that can affect rheological behavior. Special measuring instruments and equipment are available, if needed.

Examples of further influences over rheological behavior:
- Environmental pressure (e.g. overpressure up to 1000 bar = 100 MPa)
- Magnetic field or electric field strength
- UV light rays (ultraviolet) with controlled intensity of radiation
- Relative humidity (e.g. from 5 to 95 %)

Joe Flow would like to thank everybody who accompanied him on the stroll along Rheology Road.
It was probably impossible to answer all questions about rheology and rheometry here. But hopefully, you have the feeling that the time you have spent looking, reading and thinking has been worthwhile. Joe Flow's ultimate aim is to provide all users of

rheometers with the information you need, in order to measure samples in a meaningful way, to obtain useful results, and to be able to classify and evaluate these results properly. Or, to say it in a more illustrative way:

Joe Flow would be pleased if he has helped you find the right place on Rheology Road for each and every sample you test in the future.

Appendix

Symbols, signs, abbreviations and Greek characters used

a	(m)	dimension (e.g. cone-tip truncation for CP measuring geometries, or sample thickness)
A	(m^2)	area (e.g. shear area, or cross-sectional area of a solid sample)
b	(m)	dimension (e.g. sample width)
BCE		before common era
CC		concentric cylinders (measuring geometry)
cP		centi-poise (old unit of shear viscosity)
CP		cone-and-plate or cone/plate (measuring geometry)
CP	(°C)	cloud point (oil)
CSD		controlled shear deformation (or CD)
CSR		controlled shear rate (or CR)
CSS		controlled shear stress (or CS)
cSt		centi-stokes (old unit of kinematic viscosity)
d	(m)	diameter (e.g. dimension of a particle)
d_0	(m)	initial diameter
DG		double gap (measuring system)
DMA		dynamic-mechanical analysis
DMTA		dynamic-mechanical thermal analysis
e		Euler's number (e = 2.718)
E	(Pa)	elasticity modulus, Young's modulus, tensile modulus
E^*	(Pa)	complex elasticity modulus (E star, e.g. as tensile modulus)
E'	(Pa)	storage modulus (in tension), elastic modulus (in tension), (E prime)
E''	(Pa)	loss modulus (in tension), viscous modulus (in tension), (E double prime)
F	(N)	force (e.g. as shear force or tensile force)
FTS		frequency/temperature shift
G	(Pa)	shear modulus
G^*	(Pa)	complex shear modulus (G star)
G'	(Pa)	storage modulus (in shear), elastic shear modulus, (G prime)
G''	(Pa)	loss modulus (in shear), viscous shear modulus, (G double prime)

h	(m)	gap distance (two-plates model), width of shear gap
H	(m)	gap distance (PP measuring geometry)
HB		Herschel / Bulkley (flow-curve-fitting model)
HSV		high-shear viscosity
KU		Krebs units, using Krebs spindles
L	(m)	length (e.g. length of a (solid) sample)
L_0	(m)	initial length
LE		linear elastic
LSV		low-shear viscosity
LVE		linear viscoelastic
M	(g/mol)	(average) molar mass
M	(Nm)	torque
M_A	(Nm)	amplitude of the torque
MMD		molar-mass distribution
MSV		medium-shear viscosity
n	(min^{-1})	rotational speed
NLGI		grease classification (*National Lubricating Grease Institute*)
ORO		oscillation / rotation / oscillation (step test)
p	(-)	parameter of the Herschel/Bulkley flow-curve-fitting model
P		poise (old unit of shear viscosity)
PDMS		silicone (polydimethyl siloxane)
PMB		polymer modified bitumen
PP		plate/plate or parallel plates (measuring geometries)
PP	(°C)	pour point (oil)
R	(m)	radius (measuring geometries, pipeline)
R_e	(m)	radius of measuring cup (cylinder geometries, e for external)
R_i	(m)	radius of measuring bob (cylinder geometries, i for internal)
s	(m)	path, deflection path
SI units		(International system of units, French: système international d'unités)
SMD		surface-mounted devices (electronics industry)
St		stokes (old unit of kinematic viscosity)
t	(s)	time
t_{CR}	(s)	time-point of the beginning of a chemical reaction
t_{MP}	(s)	measuring-point duration
t_S	(s)	starting time (e.g. for gel formation or a curing process)
t_{SG}	(s)	time-point of the sol/gel transition (gel point)
t_V	(s)	time until a certain viscosity has been reached (e.g. for gel formation or a curing process)
TTS		time/temperature shift
T_{CR}	(°C)	temperature at the beginning of a chemical reaction
T_g	(°C)	glass-transition temperature
T_k	(°C)	crystallization temperature
T_m	(°C)	melting temperature
v	(m/s)	velocity, speed

V (m^3) volume

Greek letters

α	(°) or (rad)	cone angle of a cone/plate measuring geometry (alpha)
α	(°) or (rad)	internal angle at the tip of the bob of a cylinder geometry (alpha)
δ	(°)	phase-shift angle (delta)
$\tan\delta$	(1)	loss factor, damping factor (tangent delta)
ε	(1) or in (%)	extensional strain or elongation (epsilon)
ε_A	(1) or in (%)	extensional-strain amplitude (epsilon A)
ε_H	(1) or in (%)	Hencky strain (epsilon)
$\dot{\varepsilon}$	(s^{-1})	extensional-strain rate (epsilon dot)
$\dot{\varepsilon}_H$	(s^{-1})	Hencky strain rate (epsilon dot)
γ	(1) or in (%)	shear strain or shear deformation (gamma)
γ_A	(1) or in (%)	strain amplitude or deformation amplitude (gamma A)
γ_{co}	(1) or in (%)	shear deformation at the crossover point of G' and G'' (gamma co)
γ_L	(1) or in (%)	shear deformation at the limit of the LVE region, linearity limit of shear strain (gamma L)
$\dot{\gamma}$	(s^{-1})	shear rate (gamma dot)
φ	(°) or (rad)	deflection angle (phi)
φ_A	(°) or (rad)	amplitude of the deflection angle (phi A)
η	(Pas)	(shear) viscosity (eta)
η_E	(Pas)	extensional viscosity (eta E)
η_E^+	(Pas)	time-dependent extensional viscosity (eta E plus)
η_{min}	(Pas)	viscosity minimum (eta min)
η_0	(Pas)	zero-shear viscosity or limiting low-shear viscosity (eta zero)
η_∞	(Pas)	limiting high-shear viscosity (eta infinite)
η^*	(Pas)	complex viscosity (eta star)
λ	(s)	relaxation time (lambda)
μ	(1)	Poisson's ratio (mu)
ν	(m^2/s)	kinematic viscosity (nu)
π		circle constant ($\pi = 3.142$), (pi)
ρ	(kg/m^3)	density (rho)
σ	(Pa)	tensile stress (sigma)
σ_A	(Pa)	tensile-stress amplitude (sigma A)
τ_{co}	(Pa)	shear stress at the crossover point (tau co)
τ	(Pa)	shear stress (tau)
τ_A	(Pa)	shear-stress amplitude (tau A)
τ_f	(Pa)	flow stress, flow point
τ_L	(Pa)	linearity limit of shear stress (or yield stress)
τ_y	(Pa)	yield stress, yield point (or linearity limit of shear stress)
τ_0	(Pa)	yield point (via flow curve)
τ_1	(Pa)	yield point (via γ/τ diagram, as limit of the LE region)
τ_2	(Pa)	yield point (via γ/τ diagram, as crossover point of fitting lines)
ω	(rad/s) or (s^{-1})	angular frequency (omega)

Units

The seven **SI base units** are (SI means – in French – système international d'unités): **m** (meter, length), **kg** (kilogram, mass), **s** (second, time), **K** (kelvin, temperature or °C, degree celsius), **A** (ampere, electric current), **mol** (amount of substance, 1 mol is equal to $6.022 \cdot 10^{23}$ atoms, Avogadro constant), **cd** (candela, light intensity)

length L (ISO unit: m)
1 m = 100 cm (centimeter) = 1000 mm
1 mm (millimeter) = 10^{-3} m = 1000 μm
1 μm (micrometer) = 10^{-6} m = 1000 nm
1 nm (nanometer) = 10^{-9} m
(obsolete: 1 in (inch) = 25.4 mm)

area A (ISO unit: m^2)
1 m^2 = 10^4 cm^2 = 10^6 mm^2

volume V (ISO unit: m^3)
1 m^3 = 10^6 cm^3 = 10^9 mm^3 = 1000 l (liter)
1 cm^3 = 1 ml (milliliter)

mass m (ISO unit: kg)
1 kg = 1000 g (gram) = 10^6 mg (milligram)

density ρ (ISO unit: kg/m^3)
1000 kg/m^3 = 1 g/cm^3 = 1 g/ml = 1 kg/l
1 kg/m^3 = 1 g/l

force F (ISO unit: N)
1 N (newton) = 1 $(kg \cdot m)/s^2$

torque M (ISO unit: Nm)
1 Nm (newton meter) = 1000 mNm (milli-Nm) = 10^6 μNm (micro-Nm) = 10^9 nNm (nano-Nm)
1 Nm = 1 $(kg \cdot m^2)/s^2$

shear stress τ **and pressure p** (ISO unit: Pa)
1 Pa (pascal) = 1 N/m^2 = 1 $kg/(m \cdot s^2)$
1 kPa (kilo-pascal) = 1000 Pa
1 MPa (mega-pascal) = 10^6 Pa = 1000 kPa
1 GPa (giga-pascal) = 10^9 Pa = 1000 MPa
1 hPa (hecto-pascal) = 100 Pa = 1 mbar (millibar) = 10^{-3} bar
1 bar = 10^5 Pa = 0.1 MPa (mega-pascal)
(obsolete: 1 psi (pound per square inch) = 6890 Pa)

time t (ISO unit: s)
1 s = 1000 ms (millisecond)
60 s = 1 min
1 h (hour) = 60 min = 3600 s

velocity v (ISO unit: m/s)
1 m/s = 60 m/min = 3.6 km/h (kilometers per hour)
1 km/h = 0.278 m/s

angle φ (recommended unit: rad)
1 rad = 1000 mrad (millirad)
The following holds: 360° (degree) = 2π rad
1 rad = 360°/2π = 57.3°
1° = 17.5 mrad

rotational speed n and angular velocity ω (ISO unit: rad/s or s^{-1})
Conversion: ω (rad/s) = ($2\pi \cdot n$) / 60, with n in min^{-1}
ω can be stated in rad/s or in 1/s = 1 s^{-1}
1 min^{-1} = 1/min = 0.0167 s^{-1}
1 rad/s = 9.55 min^{-1}
(obsolete: 1 rpm, revolutions per minute)

frequency f and angular frequency ω (ISO unit: rad/s or s^{-1})
frequency f: 1 Hz (hertz) is equivalent to one cycle per second
(in linear direction or on a circular path)
angular frequency ω: 1 rad/s is equivalent to a rotational oscillation
with an angle of rotation of 1 rad per s
Conversion: ω (in rad/s) = $2\pi \cdot f$ (in Hz)
ω can be stated in rad/s or in 1/s = 1 s^{-1}
1 Hz = 6.28 rad/s
1 rad/s = 0.159 Hz

temperature T (ISO unit: K, but °C is more useful in practice)
T (in K) = T (in °C) + 273, with K (kelvin) and °C (degree celsius)
T (in °C) = T (in K) – 273
T (in °C) = (5/9) · (T (in °F) - 32), with °F (degree fahrenheit; this is not an SI unit)
T (in °F) = (9/5) · (T (in °C) + 32)

energy E (ISO unit: J)
1 J (joule) = 1 Nm = 1 $(kg \cdot m^2)/s^2$
(obsolete: 1 kcal = 4.19 kJ)
(obsolete: 1 kWh = 3600 kJ)

kinematic viscosity ν (ISO unit: m^2/s)

$1\ m^2/s = 10^6\ mm^2/s = 10^4\ cm^2/s$

(obsolete: $1\ St\ (stokes) = 100\ cSt = 1\ cm^2/s = 10^{-4}\ m^2/s$)

(obsolete: $1\ cSt\ (centi\text{-}stokes) = 1\ mm^2/s = 10^{-6}\ m^2/s$)

shear viscosity η (ISO unit: Pas)

$1\ Pas\ (pascal\ second) = 1000\ mPas\ (milli\text{-}pascal\ second) = 1\ kg/(m{\cdot}s)$

(obsolete: $1\ P\ (poise) = 100\ cP = 0.1\ Pas$, best pronounced in French)

(obsolete: $1\ cP\ (centi\text{-}poise) = 1\ mPas = 10^{-3}\ Pas$)

References and Standards

References

[1] Anton Paar GmbH: e-learning course (on CD) - Basics of Rheometry, part 1: Rotation; part 2: Oscillation; Basics of Viscometry. Graz, 2010

[2] BASF SE: Calendar. Ludwigshafen, 2013

[3] Barnes, H.A., Hutton, J.F., Walters, K.: An introduction to rheology. Elsevier, Amsterdam, 1989. Barnes, H.A.: A handbook of elementary rheology. Inst. of Non-Newt. Fluid Mechanics, Aberystwyth, 2000. Barnes, H.A.: Viscosity. INNFM, Aberystwyth, 2000

[4] Boger, D.V., Walters, K.: Rheological phenomena in focus. Elsevier, Amsterdam, 1993

[5] Degussa AG: Schriftenreihe Pigmente (Nr. 18). Frankfurt/Main

[6] Macosko, C.W.: Rheology, principles, measurements, and applications. Wiley, New York, 1994

[7] Meichsner, G., Mezger, T.G., Schröder, J.: Lackeigenschaften messen und steuern. Vincentz, Hannover, 2016 (2nd edition)

[8] Mezger, T.G.: Das Rheologie-Handbuch. Vincentz, Hannover, 2016 (5th edition); The Rheology-Handbook. Vincentz, Hanover, 2020 (5th edition)

[9] Ottersbach, J.: Bedruckstoff und Farbe. Beruf + Schule, Itzehoe, 1995 (3rd edition)

[10] Pahl, M., Gleissle, W., Laun, H.M.: Praktische Rheologie für Kunststoffe und Elastomere. VDI, Düsseldorf, 1995

[11] Tanner, R.I., Walters, K.: Rheology – an historical perspective. Elsevier, Amsterdam, 1998

[12] Teschner, H.: Offsetdrucktechnik. Fachschriftenverlag, Fellbach, 1997 (10th edition)

[13] Durou, J.-M.: Céremonie du Thé, Mauritanie. Nouvelles Images S.A., Lombreuil, 2001

[14] Society of Cosmetic Chemists, North America

[15] DIN-Taschenbuch 398: Rheologie, ed. DIN e.V., Beuth, Berlin, 2019 (2th ed.)

Standards cited

For an extensive list of rheology and rheometry standards, please see [8], above.

ISO 2431: Paints and varnishes: Flow time by use of flow cups. 2019

ISO 2555: Plastics (resins in the liquid state or as emulsions or dispersions): Apparent viscosity using a single cylinder type rotational viscometer method. 2018

ISO 3219: Rheology (rotational and oscillatory rheometry). Part 1: Vocabulary and symbols. 2021; Part 2: General principles. 2021

ISO 6721: Plastics: Dynamic mechanical properties. Part 1: General principles. 2019. Part 2: Torsion-pendulum method (torsional tests). 2008. Part 10: Complex shear viscosity using a parallel-plate oscillatory rheometer (for polymer melts). 2015

ISO 12058: Plastics: Viscosity using a falling-ball viscometer. Part 1: Inclined-tube method. 2018

ASTM D1200: Viscosity by Ford Viscosity Cup. 2010 (2018)

ASTM D4065: Plastics: Dynamic mechanical properties. 2020

ASTM D4092: Terminology for plastics: Dynamic mechanical properties. 2007 (2013)

ASTM D7175: Rheological properties of asphalt binder by dynamic shear rheometer (DSR). 2015

ASTM E1640: Glass transition temperature (T_g) by dynamic mechanical analysis (DMA). 2018

For an extensive list of DIN standards on rheology and rheometry, please see [8] and [15], above.

EN 14770: Bitumen and bituminous binders: Complex shear modulus and phase angle using a Dynamic Shear Rheometer (DSR). 2012

EN 17408: Flowability and application behaviour of viscoelastic adhesives using the oscillatory rheometry. 2020

DIN 51810: Lubricants: Part 1: Shear viscosity of lubricating greases using rotational viscometers and cone/plate systems. 2017. Part 2: Flow point using oscillatory rheometers and parallel-plate measuring systems. 2017

DIN 53015: Viscosity using the rolling ball viscometer according to Höppler. 2019

DIN 53019: Viscometry/rheometry: Viscosities and flow curves / rheological properties using rotational viscometers - Part 1: Principles and measuring geometries. 2008. Part 4: Rheometry: Oscillatory rheology. 2016.

DIN/TR 91143 - Rheological test methods: Part 1: Yield point. 2021. Part 2: Thixotropy - time-dependent structural change. 2021

Index

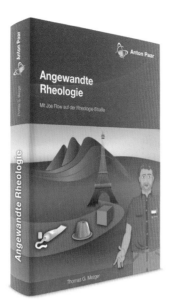

German version
(1st edition of 2014-07; 6th ed. of 2021-10)

Angewandte Rheologie
Mit Joe Flow auf der Rheologie Straße
(200 p.), ISBN 978-3-200-03652-9

Chinese version
(1st edition of 2016-03; 3rd ed. of 2020-08)

应用流变学
与 Joe Flow 一起探索流变之路
(196 p.), ISBN 978-3-9504016-2-2

Japanese version
(1st edition of 2020-07)

応用レオロジー
ジョー・フローとレオロジーロードを歩く
(196 p.), ISBN 978-3-9504016-8-4

Korean version
(1st edition of 2016-09; 3rd ed. of 2021-01)

응용 유변학
김 유변 선생님과 함께 하는
"유변학 거리" 산책
(194 p.), ISBN 978-3-9504016-3-9

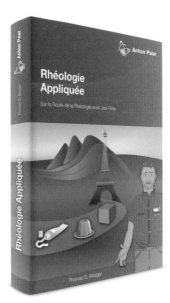

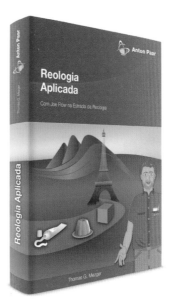

French version
(1st edition of 2017-05; 3rd ed. of 2020-10)

Rhéologie Appliquée
Sur la Route de la Rhéologie avec Joe Flow
(196 p.), ISBN 978-3-9504016-4-6

Portuguese version
(1st edition of 2018-10; 2nd ed. 2020-10)

Reologia Aplicada
Com Joe Flow na Estrada da Reologia
(196 p.), ISBN 978-3-9504016-6-0

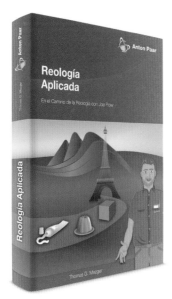

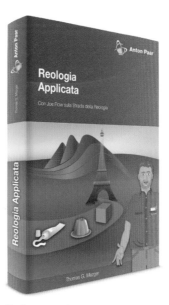

Spanish version
(1st edition of 2018-10)

Reología Aplicada
En el Camino de la Reología con Joe Flow
(196 p.), ISBN 978-3-9504016-5-3

Italian version
(1st edition of 2019-12)

Reologia Applicata
Con Joe Flow sulla Strada della Reologia
(200 p.), ISBN 978-3-9504016-7-7